THE
EINSTEIN THEORY
OF
RELATIVITY

Books by L. R. and H. G. Lieber

NON-EUCLIDEAN GEOMETRY
GALOIS AND THE THEORY OF GROUPS
THE EDUCATION OF T. C. MITS
THE EINSTEIN THEORY OF RELATIVITY

THE
EINSTEIN THEORY
OF
RELATIVITY

Text By
LILLIAN R. LIEBER

Drawings By
HUGH GRAY LIEBER

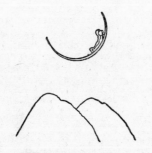

RINEHART & COMPANY, INC.

New York   Toronto

To

FRANKLIN DELANO ROOSEVELT

who saved the world from those forces
of evil which sought to destroy
Art and Science and the very
Dignity of Man.

PREFACE

In this book on the Einstein Theory of Relativity
the attempt is made
to introduce just enough
mathematics
to HELP
and NOT to HINDER
the lay reader;
"lay" can of course apply to
various domains of knowledge —
perhaps then we should say:
the layman in Relativity.

Many "popular" discussions of
Relativity,
without any mathematics at all,
have been written.
But we doubt whether
even the best of these
can possibly give to a novice
an adequate idea of
what it is all about.
What is very clear when expressed
in mathematical language
sounds "mystical" in
ordinary language.

On the other hand,
there are many discussions,
including Einstein's own papers,
which are accessible to the
experts only.

We believe that
there is a class of readers
who can get very little out of
either of these two kinds of
discussion —
readers who know enough about
mathematics
to follow a simple mathematical presentation
of a domain new to them,
built from the ground up,
with sufficient details to
bridge the gaps that exist
FOR THEM
in both
the popular and the expert
presentations.

This book is an attempt
to satisfy the needs of
this kind of reader.

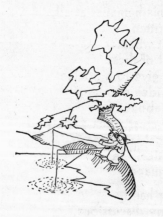

CONTENTS

Part I
THE SPECIAL THEORY

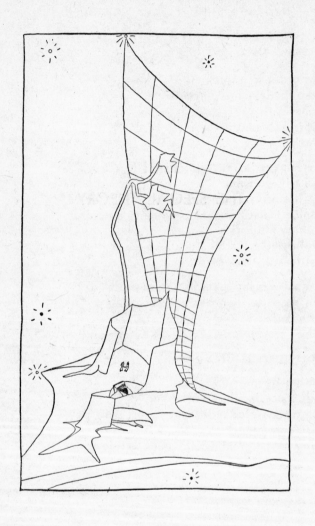

I. INTRODUCTION.

In order to appreciate
the fundamental importance
of Relativity,
it is necessary to know
how it arose.

Whenever a "revolution" takes place,
in any domain,
it is always preceded by
some maladjustment producing a tension,
which ultimately causes a break,
followed by a greater stability —
at least for the time being.

What was the maladjustment in Physics
in the latter part of the 19th century,
which led to the creation of
the "revolutionary" Relativity Theory?

Let us summarize it briefly:

It has been assumed that
all space is filled with ether,*
through which radio waves and light waves
are transmitted —
any modern child talks quite glibly

*This ether is of course NOT the chemical ether
  which surgeons use!
  It is not a liquid, solid, or gas,
  it has never been seen by anybody,
  its presence is only conjectured
  because of the need for some medium
  to transmit radio and light waves.

about "wave-lengths"
in connection with the radio.

Now, if there is an ether,
does it surround the earth
and travel with it,
or does it remain stationary
while the earth travels through it?

Various known facts* indicate that
the ether does NOT travel with the earth.
If, then, the earth is moving THROUGH the ether,
there must be an "ether wind,"
just as a person riding on a bicycle
through still air,
feels an air wind blowing in his face.

And so an experiment was performed
by Michelson and Morley (see p. 8)
in 1887,
to detect this ether wind;
and much to the surprise of everyone,
no ether wind was observed.

This unexpected result was explained by
a Dutch physicist, Lorentz, in 1895,
in a way which will be described
in Chapter II.
The search for the ether wind
was then resumed
by means of other kinds of experiments.†

*See the article "Aberration of Light",
  by A. S. Eddington,
  in the Encyclopedia Britannica, 14th ed.
†See the article "Relativity"
  by James Jeans,
  also in the Enc. Brit. 14th ed.

themselves.

ormed
result.

of the experiment

ng simple problem,

studied

current flowing with

dicated by the arrow:

B

w would take longer —
ma swim
A and back to A ,

lish in the
osocal Magazine, vol. 24, (1887).

But, again and again,
to the consternation of the physicists,
no ether wind could be detected,
until it seemed that
nature was in a "conspiracy"
to prevent our finding this effect!

At this point
Einstein took up the problem,
and decided that
a natural "conspiracy"
must be a natural LAW operating.
And to answer the question
as to what is this law,
he proposed his Theory of Relativity,
published in two papers,
one in 1905 and the other in 1915.*

He first found it necessary to
re-examine the fundamental ideas
upon which classical physics was based,
and proposed certain vital changes in them.
He then made
A VERY LIMITED NUMBER OF
MOST REASONABLE ASSUMPTIONS
from which he deduced his theory.
So fruitful did his analysis prove to be
that by means of it he succeeded in:

(1) Clearing up the fundamental ideas.
(2) Explaining the Michelson-Morley experiment
      in a much more rational way than
      had previously been done.

*Both now published in one volume
 including also the papers by
 Lorentz and Minkowski,
 to which we shall refer later;
 see SOME INTERESTING READING, page 324.

(3) Doing away with
other outstanding difficulties
in physics.
(4) Deriving a
NEW LAW OF GRAVITATION
much more adequate than the
Newtonian one
(See Part II.: The General Theory)
and which led to several
important predictions
which could be verified by experiment;
and which have been so verified
since then.
(5) Explaining
QUITE INCIDENTALLY
a famous discrepancy in astronomy
which had worried the astronomers
for many years
(This also is discussed in
The General Theory).

Thus, the Theory of Relativity had
a profound philosophical bearing
on ALL of physics,
as well as explaining
many SPECIFIC outstanding difficulties
that had seemed to be entirely
UNRELATED,
and of further increasing our knowledge
of the physical world
by suggesting a number of
NEW experiments which have led to
NEW discoveries.

No other physical theory
has been so powerful
though based on so FEW assumptions.

As we shall see.

or
from A to C and back to A,
if the distances AB and AC are equal,
AB being parallel to the current,
and AC perpendicular to it?
Let the man's rate of swimming in still water
be represented by c;
then, when swimming against the current,
from A to B,
his rate would be only $c - v$,
whereas,
when swimming with the current,
from B back to A,
his rate would, of course, be $c + v$.
Therefore the time required
to swim from A to B
would be $a/(c - v)$,
where a represents the distance AB;
and the time required
for the trip from B to A
would be $a/(c + v)$.
Consequently,
the time for the round trip would be

$$t_1 = a/(c - v) + a/(c + v)$$
or $\qquad t_1 = 2ac/(c^2 - v^2).$

Now let us see
how long the round trip
from A to C and back to A
would take.
If he headed directly toward C,
the current would carry him downstream,
and he would land at some point
to the left of C in the figure on p. 8.
Therefore,
in order to arrive at C,

9

he should head for some point D
just far enough upstream
to counteract the effect of the current.

In other words,
if the water could be kept still
until he swam at his own rate c
from A to D,
and then the current
were suddenly allowed to operate,
carrying him at the rate v from D to C
(without his making any further effort),
then the effect would obviously be the same
as his going directly from A to C
with a velocity equal to $\sqrt{c^2 - v^2}$,
as is obvious from the right triangle:

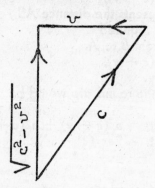

Consequently,
the time required
for the journey from A to C
would be $a/\sqrt{c^2 - v^2}$,
where a is the distance from A to C.
Similarly,
in going back from C to A,
it is easy to see that,

by the same method of reasoning,
the time would again be $a/\sqrt{c^2 - v^2}$.
Hence the time for the round trip
from A to C and back to A,
would be

$$t_2 = 2a/\sqrt{c^2 - v^2}.$$

In order to compare t_1 and t_2 more easily,
let us write β for $c/\sqrt{c^2 - v^2}$.
Then we get:

$$t_1 = 2a\beta^2/c$$
and $$t_2 = 2a\beta/c.$$

Assuming that v is less than c,
and $c^2 - v^2$ being obviously less than c^2,
the $\sqrt{c^2 - v^2}$ is therefore less than c,
and consequently β is greater than 1
(since the denominator
is less than the numerator).
Therefore t_1 is greater than t_2,
that is,
IT TAKES LONGER TO
SWIM UPSTREAM AND BACK
THAN TO SWIM THE SAME DISTANCE
ACROSS-STREAM AND BACK.

But what has all this to do
with the Michelson-Morley experiment?
In that experiment,
a ray of light was sent from A to B:

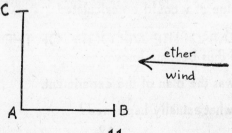

At B there was a mirror
which reflected the light back to A,
so that the ray of light
makes the round trip from A to B and back,
just as the swimmer did
in the problem described above.
Now, since the entire apparatus
shares the motion of the earth,
which is moving through space,
supposedly through a stationary ether,
thus creating an ether wind
in the opposite direction,
(namely, the direction indicated above),
this experiment seems entirely analogous
to the problem of the swimmer.
And, therefore, as before,

$$t_1 = 2a\beta^2/c \tag{1}$$
and $\qquad t_2 = 2a\beta/c.$ $\tag{2}$

Where c is now the velocity of light,
and t_2 is the time required for the light
to go from A to C and back to A
(being reflected from another mirror at C).
If, therefore,
t_1 and t_2 are found experimentally, —
then by dividing (1) by (2),
the value of β would be easily obtained.
And since $\beta = c/\sqrt{c^2 - v^2}$,
c being the known velocity of light,
the value of v could be calculated.
That is,
THE ABSOLUTE VELOCITY OF THE EARTH
would thus become known.

Such was the plan of the experiment.

Now what actually happened?

12

The experimental values of t_1 and t_2
were found to be the SAME,
instead of t_1 being greater than t_2 !
Obviously this was a most disturbing result,
quite out of harmony
with the reasoning given above.
The Dutch physicist, Lorentz,
then suggested the following explanation
of Michelson's strange result:
Lorentz suggested that
matter, owing to its electrical structure,
SHRINKS WHEN IT IS MOVING,
and this contraction occurs
ONLY IN THE DIRECTION OF MOTION.*
The AMOUNT of shrinkage
he assumes to be in the ratio of $1/\beta$
(where β has the value $c/\sqrt{c^2 - v^2}$, as before).
Thus a sphere of one inch radius
becomes an ellipsoid when it is moving,
with its shortest semi-axis
(now only $1/\beta$ inches long)

*The two papers by Lorentz on this subject
are included in the volume mentioned in
the footnote on page 5.
In the first of these papers
Lorentz mentions that the explanation proposed here
occurred also to Fitzgerald.
Hence it is often referred to as
the "Fitzgerald contraction" or
the "Lorentz contraction" or
the "Lorentz-Fitzgerald contraction."

in the direction of motion,
thus:

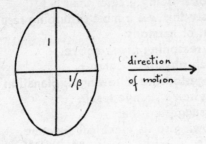

Applying this idea
to the Michelson-Morley experiment,
the distance AB (= a) on p. 8,
becomes a/β,
and t_1 becomes $2a\beta/c$,
instead of $2a\beta^2/c$,
so that now $t_1 = t_2$,
just as the experiment requires.

One might ask how it is
that Michelson did not
observe the shrinkage?
Why did not his measurements show
that AB was shorter than AC
(See the figure on p. 8)?
The obvious answer is that
the measuring rod itself contracts
when applied to AB,
so that one is not aware of the shrinkage.

To this explanation
of the Michelson-Morley experiment
the natural objection may be raised
that an explanation which is invented
for the express purpose

14

of smoothing out a certain difficulty,
and assumes a correction
of JUST the right amount,
is too artificial to be satisfying.
And Poincaré, the French mathematician,
raised this very natural objection.

Consequently,
Lorentz undertook to examine
his contraction hypothesis
in other connections,
to see whether it is in harmony also
with facts other than
the Michelson-Morley experiment.
He then published a second paper in 1904,
giving the result of this investigation.
To present this result in a clear form
let us first re-state the argument
as follows:

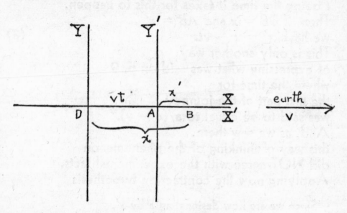

Consider a set of axes, X and Y,
supposed to be fixed in the stationary ether,
and another set X' and Y' ,
attached to the earth and moving with it,

with velocity v, as indicated above.
Let X' move along X,
and Y' move parallel to Y.

Now suppose an observer on the earth,
say Michelson,
is trying to measure
the time it takes a ray of light
to travel from A to B,
both A and B being fixed points on
the moving axis X'.
At the moment
when the ray of light starts at A
suppose that Y and Y' coincide,
and A coincides with D;
and while the light has been traveling to B
the axis Y' has moved the distance vt,
and B has reached the position
shown in the figure on p. 15,
t being the time it takes for this to happen.
Then, if $DB = x$ and $AB = x'$,
we have $x' = x - vt$.   (3)
This is only another way
of expressing what was said on p. 9
where the time for
the first part of the journey
was said to be equal to $a/(c - v)$.*
And, as we saw there,
this way of thinking of the phenomenon
did NOT agree with the experimental facts.
Applying now the contraction hypothesis

*Since we are now designating a by x',
 we have $x'/(c - v) = t$, or $x' = ct - vt$.
 But the distance the light has traveled
 is x,
 and $x = ct$,
 consequently $x' = x - vt$ is equivalent to $a/(c - v) = t$.

16

proposed by Lorentz,
x' should be divided by β ,
so that equation (3) becomes

$$x'/\beta = x - vt$$
or $\qquad x' = \beta\,(x - vt).$ \hfill (4)

Now when Lorentz examined other facts,
as stated on p. 15,
he found that equation (4)
was quite in harmony with all these facts,
but that he was now obliged
to introduce a further correction
expressed by the equation

$$t' = \beta\,(t - vx/c^2),\hfill (5)$$

where β , t , v , x , and c
have the same meaning as before —
But what is t'?!
Surely the time measurements
in the two systems are not different:
Whether the origin is at D or at A
should not affect the
TIME-READINGS.
In other words, as Lorentz saw it,
t' was a sort of "artificial" time
introduced only for mathematical reasons,
because it helped to give results
in harmony with the facts.
But obviously t' had for him
NO PHYSICAL MEANING.
As Jeans, the English physicist, puts it:
"If the observer could be persuaded
to measure time in this artificial way,
setting his clocks wrong to begin with
and then making them gain or lose permanently,
the effect of his supposed artificiality

17

would just counterbalance
the effects of his motion
through the ether"!*
Thus,
the equations finally proposed by Lorentz
are:

$$x' = \beta (x - vt)$$
$$y' = y$$
$$z' = z$$
$$t' = \beta (t - vx/c^2).$$

Note that
since the axes attached to the earth (p. 15)
are moving along the X-axis,
obviously the values of y and z
(z being the third dimension)
are the same as y' and z' , respectively.

The equations just given
are known as
THE LORENTZ TRANSFORMATION,
since they show how to transform
a set of values of x , y , z , t
into a set x', y', z', t'
in a coordinate system
moving with constant velocity v,
along the X-axis,
with respect to the
unprimed coordinate system.
And, as we saw,
whereas the Lorentz transformation
really expressed the facts correctly,
it seemed to have
NO PHYSICAL MEANING,

*See the article on Relativity in the
  Encyclopedia Britannica, 14th edition.

19

and was merely
a set of empirical equations.

Let us now see what Einstein did.

III. RE-EXAMINATION OF THE FUNDAMENTAL IDEAS.

As Einstein regarded the situation,
the negative result of
the Michelson-Morley experiment,
as well as of other experiments
which seemed to indicate a "conspiracy"
on the part of nature
against man's efforts to obtain
knowledge of the physical world (see p. 5),
these negative results,
according to Einstein,
did not merely demand
explanations of a certain number
of isolated difficulties,
but the situation was so serious
that a complete examination
of fundamental ideas
was necessary.
In other words,
he felt that there was something
fundamentally and radically wrong
in physics,
rather than a mere superficial difficulty.
And so he undertook to re-examine
such fundamental notions as
our ideas of
LENGTH and TIME and MASS.
His exceedingly reasonable examination

is most illuminating,
as we shall now see.

But first let us remind the reader
why length, time and mass
are fundamental.
Everyone knows that
VELOCITY depends upon
the distance (or LENGTH)
traversed in a given TIME,
hence the unit of velocity
DEPENDS UPON
the units of LENGTH and TIME.
Similarly,
since acceleration is
the change in velocity in a unit of time,
hence the unit of acceleration
DEPENDS UPON
the units of velocity and time,
and therefore ultimately upon
the units of LENGTH and TIME.
Further,
since force is measured
by the product of
mass and acceleration,
the unit of force
DEPENDS UPON
the units of mass and acceleration,
and hence ultimately upon
the units of
MASS, LENGTH and TIME.
And so on.
In other words,
all measurements in physics
depend primarily on
MASS, LENGTH and TIME.
That is why

21

the system of units ordinarily used
is called the "C.G.S." system,
where C stands for "centimeter"
(the unit of length),
G stands for "gram" (the unit of mass),
and S stands for "second" (the unit of time),
these being the fundamental units
from which all the others are derived.

Let us now return to
Einstein's re-examination of
these fundamental units.
Suppose that two observers
wish to compare their measurements of time.
If they are near each other
they can, of course, look at each other's watches
and compare them.
If they are far apart,
they can still compare each other's readings
BY MEANS OF SIGNALS,
say light signals or radio signals,
that is, any "electromagnetic wave"
which can travel through space.
Let us, therefore, imagine that
one observer, E, is on the earth,
and the other, S, on the sun;
and imagine that signals are sent
as follows:
By his own watch, S sends a message to E
which reads "twelve o'clock;"
E receives this message
say, eight minutes later;[*]

*Since the sun is about 93 000 000 miles
  from the earth,
  and light travels about 186 000 miles per second,
  the time for a light (or radio) signal
  to travel from the sun to the earth,
  is approximately eight minutes.

22

now, if his watch agrees with that of *S*,
it will read "12:08"
when the message arrives.
E then sends back to *S*
the message "12:08,"
and, of course,
S receives this message 8 minutes later,
namely, at 12:16.
Thus *S* will conclude,
from this series of signals,
that his watch and that of *E*
are in perfect agreement.

But let us now imagine
that the entire solar system
is moving through space,
so that both the sun and the earth
are moving in the direction
shown in the figure:

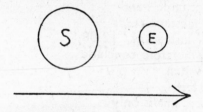

without any change in
the distance between them.
Now let the signals again be sent
as before:
S sends his message "12 o'clock,"
but since *E* is moving away from the message,
the latter will not reach *E* in 8 minutes,
but will take some longer time
to overtake *E*,
Say, 9 minutes.

23

If *E*'s watch is in agreement with that of *S*,
it will read 12:09
when the message reaches him,
and *E* accordingly sends a return message,
reading "12:09."
Now *S* is traveling toward this message,
and it will therefore reach him
in LESS than 8 minutes,
say, in 7 minutes.
Thus *S* receives *E*'s message
at 12:16,
just as before.
Now if *S* and *E* are both
UNAWARE of their motion
(and, indeed,
we are undoubtedly moving
in ways that we are entirely unaware of,
so that this assumption
is far from being an imaginary one.)
S will not understand
why *E*'s message reads
"12:09" instead of "12:08,"
and will therefore conclude
that *E*'s watch
must be fast.
Of course, this is only
an apparent error in *E*'s watch,
because, as we know,
it is really due to the motion,
and not at all
to any error in *E*'s watch.
It must be noted, however,
that this omniscient "we"
who can see exactly
what is "really" going on in the universe,
does not exist,
and that all human observers

24

are really in the situation
in which *S* is,
namely,
that of not knowing
about the motion in question,
and therefore
being OBLIGED to conclude
that *E*'s watch is wrong!

And therefore,
S sends *E* the message
telling him that
if *E* sets his clock back one minute,
then their clocks will agree.

In the same way,
suppose that other observers,
A , *B* , *C* , etc.,
all of whom are at rest WITH RESPECT TO
S and *E* ,
all set their clocks to agree with that of *S* ,
by the same method of signals described above.
They would all say then
that all their clocks are in agreement.
Whether this is absolutely true or not,
they cannot tell (see above),
but that is the best they can do.

Now let us see what will happen
when these observers wish
to measure the length of something.
To measure the length of an object,
you can place it,
say, on a piece of paper,
put a mark on the paper at one end of the object,
and another mark at the other end,
then, with a ruler,
find out how many units of length there are

between the two marks.
This is quite simple provided that
the object you are measuring and the paper
are at rest (relatively to you).
But suppose the object is
say, a fish swimming about in a tank?
To measure its length while it is in motion,
by placing two marks on the walls of the tank,
one at the head, and the other at the tail,
it would obviously be necessary
to make these two marks
SIMULTANEOUSLY —
for, otherwise,
if the mark *B* is made at a certain time,

then the fish allowed to swim
in the direction indicated by the arrow,
and then the mark at the head
is made at some later time,
when it has reached *C*,
then you would say that
the length of the fish
is the distance *BC*,
which would be a fish-story indeed!

Now suppose that our observers,
after their clocks are all in agreement (see p. 25),
undertake to measure
the length of a train

26

which is moving through their universe
with a uniform velocity.
They send out orders that
at 12 o'clock sharp,
whichever observer happens to be
at the place where
the front end of the train, A',
arrives at that moment,
to NOTE THE SPOT,
and some other observer,
who happens to be at the place where
the rear end of the train, B',
is at that same moment,
to put a mark at THAT spot.
Thus, after the train has gone,
they can, at their leisure,
measure the distance between the two marks,
this distance being equal to
the length of the train,
since the two marks were made
SIMULTANEOUSLY, namely at 12 o'clock,
their clocks being all
in perfect agreement with each other.

Let us now talk to the people on the train.
Suppose, first,
that they are unaware of their motion,
and that, according to them,
A, B, C, etc., are the ones who are moving, —
a perfectly reasonable assumption.
And suppose that there are two clocks on the train,
one at A', the other at B',
and that these clocks
have been set in agreement with each other
by the method of signals described above.
Obviously the observers A, B, C, etc.,
will NOT admit that the clocks at A' and B'

27

are in agreement with each other,
since they "know" that the train is in motion,
and therefore the method of signals
used on the moving train
has led to an erroneous setting
of the moving clocks (see p. 25).
Whereas the people on the train,
since they "know" that
A, B, C, etc., are the ones who are moving,
claim that it is the clocks
belonging to A, B, C, etc.,
which were set wrong.

What is the result of this
difference of opinion?
When the clocks of A and B, say,
both read 12 o'clock,
and at that instant A and B
each makes a mark at a certain spot,
then A and B claim, of course,
that these marks were made
simultaneously;
but the people on the train do not admit
that the clocks of A and B
have been properly set,
and they therefore claim that
the two marks were
NOT made SIMULTANEOUSLY,
and that, therefore,
the measurement of the LENGTH of the train
is NOT correct.
Thus,
when the people on the train
make the marks
simultaneously,
as judged by their own clocks,
the distance between the two marks

28

will NOT be the same as before.

Hence we see that
MOTION
prevents agreement in the
setting of clocks,
and, as a consequence of this,
prevents agreement in the
measurement of LENGTH!

Similarly,
as we shall see on p. 79,
motion also affects
the measurement of mass —
different observers obtaining
different results
when measuring the mass of the same object.

And since,
as we mentioned on p. 21,
all other physical measurements
depend upon
length, mass, and time,
it seems that
therefore there cannot be agreement
in any measurements made
by different observers
who are moving with different velocities!

Now, of course,
observers on the earth
partake of the various motions
to which the earth is subject —
the earth turns on its axis,
it goes around the sun,
and perhaps has other motions as well.
Hence it would seem that
observations made by people on the earth

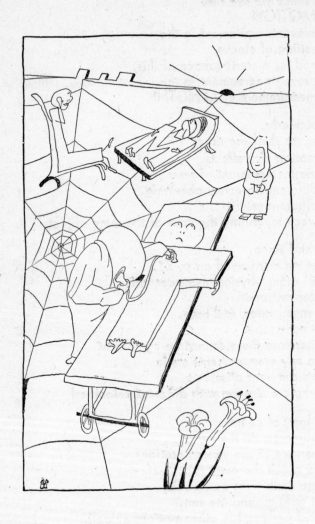

cannot agree with
those taken from
some other location in the universe,
and are therefore
not really correct
and consequently worthless!

Thus Einstein's careful and reasonable examination
led to the realization that
Physics was suffering from
no mere single ailment,
as evidenced by the
Michelson-Morley experiment alone,
but was sick from head to foot!

Did he find a remedy?

HE DID!

IV. THE REMEDY.

So far, then, we see that
THE OLD IDEAS REGARDING
THE MEASUREMENT OF
LENGTH, TIME AND MASS
involved an "idealistic" notion of
"absolute time"
which was supposed to be
the same for all observers,
and that
Einstein introduced
a more PRACTICAL notion of time
based on the actual way of
setting clocks by means of SIGNALS.
This led to the
DISCARDING of the idea that

the LENGTH of an object
is a fact about the object
and is independent of the person
who does the measuring,
since we have shown (Chapter III.)
that the measurement of length
DEPENDS UPON
THE STATE OF MOTION OF THE MEASURER.

Thus two observers,
moving relatively to each other
with uniform velocity,
DO NOT GET THE SAME VALUE
FOR THE LENGTH OF A GIVEN OBJECT.
Hence we may say that
LENGTH is NOT a FACT about an OBJECT,
but rather a
RELATIONSHIP between
the OBJECT and the OBSERVER.
And similarly for TIME and MASS (Ch. III.).
In other words,
from this point of view
it is NOT CORRECT to say:

$$x' = x - vt$$

as Michelson did* (see p. 16, equation (3)),
since this equation implies that
the value of x'
is a perfectly definite quantity,

*We do not wish to imply that
Michelson made a crude error—
ANY CLASSICAL PHYSICIST
would have made the same statement,
for those were the prevailing ideas
thoroughly rooted in everybody's mind,
before Einstein pointed out
the considerations discussed in Ch. III.

namely,
THE length of the arm *AB* of the apparatus
in the Michelson-Morley experiment
(See the diagram on p. 15).
Nor is it correct to assume that

$$t' = t$$

(again as Michelson did)
for two different observers,
which would imply that
both observers agree in their
time measurements.

These ideas were contradicted by
Michelson's EXPERIMENTS,
which were so ingeniously devised
and so precisely performed.

And so Einstein said that
instead of starting with such ideas,
and basing our reasoning on them,
let us rather
START WITH THE EXPERIMENTAL DATA,
and see to what relationships
they will lead us,
relationships between
the length and time measurements
of different observers.
Now what experimental data
must we take into account here?
They are:

FACT (1): It is impossible
to measure the "ether wind,"
or, in other words,
it is impossible to detect our motion
relative to the ether.
This was clearly shown by the

33

Michelson-Morley experiment,
as well as by all other experiments
devised to
measure this motion (see p. 5).
Indeed, this is the great
"conspiracy"
that started all the trouble,
or, as Einstein prefers to see it,
and most reasonably so,
THIS IS A FACT.

FACT (2): The velocity of light is the same
no matter whether the source of light
is moving or stationary.
Let us examine this statement
more fully,
to see exactly what it means.

To do this,
it is necessary to remind the reader
of a few well-known facts:
Imagine that we have two trains,
one with a gun on the front end,
the other with a source of sound
on the front end,
say, a whistle.
Suppose that the velocity, u ,
of a bullet shot from the gun,
happens to be the same as
the velocity of the sound.
Now suppose that both trains
are moving with the same velocity, v ,
in the same direction.
The question is:
How does the velocity of a bullet
(fired from the MOVING train)
relatively to the ground,
compare with

34

the velocity of the sound
that came from the whistle
on the other MOVING train,
relatively to the medium, the air,
in which it is traveling?
Are they the same?

No!

The velocity of the bullet,
RELATIVELY TO THE GROUND,
is $v + u$,
since the bullet is now propelled forward
not only with its own velocity, u ,
given to it by the force of the gun,
but, in addition,
has an inertial velocity, v ,
which it has acquired from
the motion of the train
and which is shared by
all objects on the train.

But in the case of the sound wave
(which is a series of pulsations,
alternate condensations and rarefactions of the air
in rapid succession),
the first condensation formed
in the neighborhood of the whistle,
travels out with the velocity u
relatively to the medium,
regardless as to whether
the train is moving or not.
So that this condensation
has only its own velocity
and does NOT have the inertial velocity
due to the motion of the train,
the velocity of the sound
depending only upon the medium

(that is, whether it is air or water, etc.,
and whether it is hot or cold, etc.),
but not upon the motion of the source
from which the sound started.

The following diagram
shows the relative positions
after one second,
in both cases:

CASE I.
Both trains at rest.

Train   u ft.   Bullet

Train   u ft.   Sound

CASE II.
Both trains moving with velocity v.

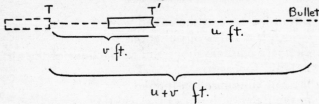

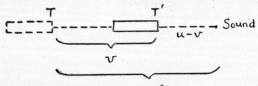

Thus, in Case II.,
the bullet has moved
$u + v$ feet in one second

36

from the starting point,
whereas the sound has moved only u feet
from the starting point,
in that one second.
Thus we see that
the velocity of sound is u feet per second
relatively to the starting point,
whether the source remains stationary
as in Case I.,
or follows the sound, as in Case II.

Expressing it algebraically,

$$x = ut$$

applies equally well for sound
in both Case I. and Case II.,
x being the distance
FROM THE STARTING POINT.
Indeed, this fact is true of ALL WAVE MOTION,
and one would therefore expect
that it would apply also to LIGHT.
As a matter of FACT,
it DOES,
and that is what is meant by
FACT (2) on p. 34.

Now, as a result of this,
it appears,
by referring again to the diagram on p. 36,
that
relatively to the MOVING train (Case II.)
we should then have,
for sound

$$x' = (u - v)t$$

x' being the distance
from T' to the point where
the sound has arrived after time t.

From which, by measuring x', u, and t,
we could then calculate v,
the velocity of the train.
And, similarly, for light
using the moving earth
instead of the moving train,
we should then have,
as a consequence of FACT (2) on p. 34,

$$x' = (c - v)t$$

where c is the velocity of light
(relatively to a stationary observer
out in space)
and v is the velocity of the earth
relatively to this stationary observer —
and hence
the ABSOLUTE velocity of the earth.

Thus we should be able
to determine v.
But this contradicts FACT (1),
according to which
it is IMPOSSIBLE to determine v.

Thus it APPEARS that
FACT (2) requires
the velocity of light
RELATIVELY TO THE MOVING EARTH
to be $c - v$ (see diagram on p. 36),
whereas FACT (1) requires it to be c.*

*FACT (1) may be re-stated as follows:
The velocity of light
RELATIVE TO A MOVING OBSERVER
(For example, an observer
on the moving earth)
must be c, and NOT $c - v$;
for otherwise,
he would be able to find v;
which is contrary to fact.

38

And so the two facts
contradict each other!
Or, stating it another way:

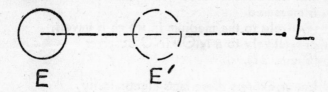

If, in one second,
the earth moves from E to E'
while a ray of light,
goes from the earth to L,
then
FACT (1) requires that
$E'L$ be equal to c (= 186,000 miles)
while FACT (2) requires that
EL be equal to c !

Now it is needless to say that
FACTS CAN NOT CONTRADICT
EACH OTHER!

Let us therefore see how,
in the light of the discussion in Ch. III.
FACTS (1) and (2) can be shown to be
NOT contradictory.

V. THE SOLUTION OF THE DIFFICULTY.

We have thus seen that
according to the facts,
the velocity of light
IS ALWAYS THE SAME,

whether the source of light
is stationary or moving
(See FACT (2) on p. 34),
and whether the velocity of light
is measured
relatively to the medium in which it travels,
or relatively to a MOVING observer
(See p. 37).

Let us express these facts algebraically,
for two observers, K and K',
who are moving with uniform velocity
relatively to each other,
thus:
K writes $x = ct$, (6)
and K' writes $x' = ct'$, (7)
both using
THE SAME VALUE FOR
THE VELOCITY OF LIGHT,
namely, c,
and each using
his own measurements of
length, x and x',
and time, t and t', respectively.

It is assumed that
at the instant when
the rays of light start on their path,
K and K' are at the SAME place,
and the rays of light
radiate out from that place
in all directions.

Now according to equation (6),
K, who is unaware of his motion through the ether
(since he cannot measure it),
may claim that he is at rest,
and that in time, t,

K' must have moved to the right,
as shown in the figure below;
and that, in the meantime,
the light,
which travels out in all directions from K,
has reached all points at
the distance ct from K,
and hence
all points on the circumference
of the circle having the radius ct.

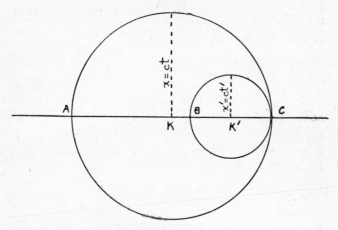

But K' claims that he is the one
who has remained stationary,
and that K, on the contrary,
has moved TO THE LEFT;
furthermore that the light travels out
from K' as a center,
instead of from K!
And this is what he means
when he says

$$x' = ct'.$$

How can they both be right?

41

We may be willing
not to take sides
in their controversy regarding the question as to
which one has moved —
K' to the right or K to the left —
because either leads to the same result.
But what about the circles?
They cannot possibly have both K and K'
as their centers!
One of them must be right and the other wrong.
This is another way of stating
the APPARENT CONTRADICTION BETWEEN
FACTS (1) and (2) (see p. 39).

Now, at last, we are ready
for the explanation.

Although K claims that
at the instant when
the light has reached the point C (p. 41),
it has also reached
the point A, on the other side,
still,
WE MUST REMEMBER THAT
when K says
two events happen simultaneously
(namely, the arrival of the light at C and A),
K' DOES NOT AGREE
THAT THEY ARE SIMULTANEOUS (see p. 28).
So that when
K' says that
the arrival of the light at C and B
(rather than at C and A)
ARE SIMULTANEOUS,
his statement
DOES NOT CONTRADICT THAT OF K,
since K and K'
DO NOT MEAN THE SAME THING

WHEN THEY SAY "SIMULTANEOUS:"
for
K's clocks at *C* and *A*
do not agree with *K'*'s clocks at *C* and *A*.
Thus when the light arrives at *A* ,
the reading of *K*'s clock there
is exactly the same as that of *K*'s clock at *C*
(*K* having set all clocks in his system
by the method of signals described on p. 25),
while
K''s clock at *A* ,
when the light arrives there,
reads a LATER TIME than his clock at *C*
when the light arrived at *C* , —
so that *K'* maintains that
the light reaches *A*
LATER than it reaches *C* ,
and NOT at the SAME instant,
as *K* claims.

Hence we see that
they are not really contradicting each other,
but that they are merely using
two different systems of clocks,
such that
the clocks in each system
agree with each other alright,
but the clocks in the one system
have NOT been set
in agreement with the clocks
in the other system (see p. 28).

That is,
if we take into account
the inevitable necessity of
using signals
in order to set clocks which are

43

at a distance from each other,
and that the arrivals of the signals
at their destinations
are influenced by
our state of motion,
of which we are not aware (p. 24),
it becomes clear that
THERE IS NO REAL CONTRADICTION HERE,
but only a difference of description
due to INEVITABLE differences
in the setting of
various systems of clocks.

We now see
in a general qualitative way,
that the situation is
not at all mysterious or unreasonable,
as it seemed to be at first.
But we must now find out
whether these considerations,
when applied QUANTITATIVELY,
actually agree with the experimental facts.

And now a pleasant surprise awaits us.

VI. THE RESULT OF APPLYING THE REMEDY.

In the last chapter we saw that
by starting with
two fundamental FACTS (p. 34),
we reached the conclusion
expressed in the equations

$$x = ct \tag{6}$$
$$\text{and} \quad x' = ct' \tag{7}$$

which are graphically represented on p. 41,
and we realized that these equations
are NOT contradictory,
(as they appear to be at first),
if we remember that there is
a difference in the setting of the clocks
in the two different systems.

We shall derive, now, from (6) and (7),
relationships between the measurements
of the two observers, K and K'.
And all the mathematics we need for this
is a little simple algebra,
such as any high school boy knows.

From (6) and (7) we get

$$x - ct = 0$$
and $$x' - ct' = 0.$$

Therefore

$$x' - ct' = \lambda(x - ct) \tag{8}$$

where λ is a constant.
Similarly, in the opposite direction,

$$x' + ct' = \mu (x + ct) \tag{9}$$

μ being another constant.
By adding and subtracting (8) and (9)

we get: $$x' = ax - bct \tag{10}$$
and $$ct' = act - bx \tag{11}$$

where $a = (\lambda + \mu)/2$ and $b = (\lambda - \mu)/2$.
Let us now find the values of a and b
in terms of v
(the relative velocity of K and K'),
and c , the velocity of light.

45

This is done in the following
ingenious manner:*
From (10)
when $x' = 0$,
then $x = bct/a$;   (12)
but $x' = 0$ at the point K':

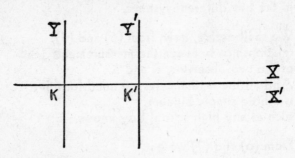

And x in this case is
the distance from K to K',
that is,
the distance traversed, in time t
by K' moving with velocity v
relatively to K.
Therefore $x = vt$.
Comparing this with (12), we get

$$v = bc/a.$$ (13)

Let us now consider the situation
from the points of view of K and K'.
Take K first:
For the time $t = 0$,
K gets $x' = ax$ (from (10)),

or $x = x'/a.$ (14)

Hence K says that

*See Appendix I in "Relativity" by Einstein,
 Pub. by Peter Smith, N. Y. (1931).

46

to get the "true" value, x,
K' should divide his x' by a;
in particular,
if $x' = 1$,
K says that K''s unit of length
is only $1/a$ of a "true" unit.

But K',
at $t' = 0$, using (11)
says

$$bx = act \qquad (15)$$

and since from (10),

$$t = (ax - x')/bc,$$

(15) becomes

$$bx = ac(ax - x')/bc,$$

or $b^2x = a^2x - ax'$,
from which

$$x' = a(1 - b^2/a^2)x. \qquad (16)$$

And since $b/a = v/c$ from (13),
(16) becomes

$$x' = a(1 - v^2/c^2)x. \qquad (17)$$

In other words,
K' says:
In order to get the "true" value, x',
K should multiply his x by

$$a(1 - v^2/c^2).$$

In particular,
if $x = 1$,
then K' says that
K's unit is really $a(1 - v^2/c^2)$ units long.
Thus

47

each observer considers that
his own measurements
are the "true" ones,
and advises the other fellow
to make a "correction."
And indeed,
although the two observers, K and K',
may express this "correction"
in different forms,
still
the MAGNITUDE of the "correction"
recommended by each of them
MUST BE THE SAME,
since it is due in both cases
to the relative motion,
only that each observer attributes this motion
to the other fellow.

Hence, from (14) and (17) we may write

$$1/a = a(1 - v^2/c^2).*$$

Solving this equation for a , we get

$$a = c/\sqrt{c^2 - v^2}.$$

*Note that this equation is
NOT obtained by
ALGEBRAIC SUBSTITUTION
from (14) and (17),
but is obtained by considering that
the CORRECTIONS advised by K and K'
in (14) and (17), respectively,
must be equal in magnitude
as pointed out above.
Thus in (14) K says:
"You must multiply your measurement by $1/a$",
whereas in (17) K' says:
"You must multiply your measurement by $a\left(1 - \frac{v^2}{c^2}\right)$";
and since these correction factors
must be equal
hence $1/a = a\left(1 - \frac{v^2}{c^2}\right)$.

Note that this value of *a*
is the same as that of β on p. 11.
Substituting in (10)
this value of *a*
and the value $bc = av$ from (13),
we get

$$x' = \beta x - \beta vt$$
or $\qquad x' = \beta(x - vt)$ (18)

which is the first of the set of equations
of the Lorentz transformation on page 19!

Furthermore,

from (18) and $\begin{cases} x = ct \\ x' = ct' \end{cases}$

we get

$$ct' = \beta(ct - vt)$$
or $\qquad t' = \beta(t - vt/c).$

Or, since $t = x/c$,

$$t' = \beta(t - vx/c^2),$$ (19)

which is another of the equations
of the Lorentz transformation!
That the remaining two equations
$y' = y$ and $z' = z$ also hold,
Einstein shows as follows:
Let K and K' each have a cylinder
of radius r, when at rest
relatively to each other,
and whose axes coincide with the X (X') axis;
Now, unless $y' = y$ and $z' = z$,
K and K' would each claim that
his own cylinder is OUTSIDE the other fellow's!

We thus see that
the Lorentz transformation was derived
by Einstein
(quite independently of Lorentz),
NOT as a set of empirical equations

devoid of physical meaning,
but, on the contrary,
as a result of
a most rational change in
our ideas regarding the measurement of
the fundamental quantities
length and time.
And so, according to him,
the first of the equations of the
Lorentz transformation,
namely,

$$x' = \beta(x - vt)$$

is so written
NOT because of any real shrinkage,
as Lorentz supposed,
but merely an apparent shrinkage,
due to the differences in
the measurements made by K and K'* (see p. 45).
And Einstein writes

$$t' = \beta(t - vx/c^2)$$

NOT because it is just a mathematical trick
WITHOUT any MEANING (see p. 19)
but again because
it is the natural consequence of
the differences in the measurements
of the two observers.

And each observer may think
that he is right
and the other one is wrong,
and yet
each one,
by using his own measurements,
arrives at the same form

---

*This shrinkage, it will be remembered,
  occurs only in the direction of motion (see p. 13).

when he expresses a physical fact,
as, for example,
when K says $x = ct$
and K' says $x' = ct'$,
they are really agreeing as to
the LAW of the propagation of light.

And similarly,
if K writes any other law of nature,
and if we apply
the Lorentz transformation
to this law,
in order to see what form the law takes
when it is expressed in terms of
the measurements made by K',
we find that
the law is still the same,
although it is now expressed
in terms of the primed coordinate system.

Hence Einstein says that
although no one knows
what the "true" measurements should be,
yet,
each observer may use his own measurements
WITH EQUAL RIGHT AND EQUAL SUCCESS
in formulating
THE LAWS OF NATURE,
or,
in formulating the
INVARIANTS of the universe,
namely, the quantities which remain unchanged
in spite of the change in measurements
due to the relative motion of K and K'.

Thus, we can now appreciate
Einstein's Principle of Relativity:
"The laws by which

the states of physical systems
undergo change,
are not affected
whether these changes of state be referred
to the one or the other
of two systems of coordinates
in uniform translatory motion."

Perhaps some one will ask
"But is not the principle of relativity old,
and was it not known long before Einstein?
Thus a person in a train
moving into a station
with uniform velocity
looks at another train which is at rest,
and imagines that the other train is moving
whereas his own is at rest.
And he cannot find out his mistake
by making observations within his train
since everything there
is just the same as it would be
if his train were really at rest.
Surely this fact,
and other similar ones,
must have been observed
long before Einstein?"

In other words,
RELATIVELY to an observer on the train
everything seems to proceed in the same way
whether his system (i.e., his train)
is at rest or in uniform* motion,
and he would therefore be unable

*Of course if the motion is not uniform,
  but "jerky",
  things on the train would jump around
  and the observer on the train
  would certainly know
  that his own train was not at rest.

to detect the motion.
Yes, this certainly was known
long before Einstein.
Let us see what connection it has
with the principle of relativity
as stated by him:

Referring to the diagram on p. 36
we see that
a bullet fired from a train
has the same velocity
RELATIVELY TO THE TRAIN
whether the latter is moving or not,
and therefore an observer on the train
could not detect the motion of the train
by making measurements on
the motion of the bullet.
This kind of relativity principle
is the one involved
in the question on page 53,
and WAS known long before Einstein.

Now Einstein
EXTENDED this principle
so that it would apply to
electromagnetic phenomena
(light or radio waves).

Thus,
according to this extension of
the principle of relativity,
an observer cannot detect
his motion through space
by making measurements on
the motion of ELECTROMAGNETIC WAVES.
But why should this extension
be such a great achievement —
why had it not been suggested before?

BECAUSE
it must be remembered that
according to fact (2) — see p. 39,

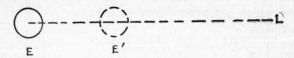

$EL = c,$
whereas,
the above-mentioned extension of
the principle of relativity
requires that $E'L$ should be equal to c
(compare the case of the bullet on p. 36).
In other words,
the extension of the principle of relativity
to electromagnetic phenomena
seems to contradict fact (2)
and therefore could not have been made
before it was shown that
fundamental measurements are merely "local"
and hence the contradiction was
only apparent,
as explained on p. 42;
so that the diagram shown above
must be interpreted
in the light of the discussion on p. 42.

Thus we see that
whereas the principle of relativity
as applied to MECHANICAL motion
(like that of the bullet)
was accepted long before Einstein,
the SEEMINGLY IMPOSSIBLE EXTENSION
of the principle
to electromagnetic phenomena
was accomplished by him.

55

This extension of the principle,
for the case in which
K and K' move relatively to each other
with UNIFORM velocity,
and which has been discussed here,
is called
the SPECIAL theory of relativity.
We shall see later
how Einstein generalized this principle
STILL FURTHER,
to the case in which
K and K' move relatively to each other
with an ACCELERATION,
that is, a CHANGING velocity.
And, by means of this generalization,
which he called
the GENERAL theory of relativity,
he derived
A NEW LAW OF GRAVITATION,
much more adequate even than
the Newtonian law,
and of which the latter
is a first approximation.

But before we can discuss this in detail
we must first see
how the ideas which we have
already presented
were put into a
remarkable mathematical form
by a mathematician named Minkowski.
This work
was essential to Einstein
in the further development of his ideas,
as we shall see.

VII. THE FOUR-DIMENSIONAL SPACE-TIME CONTINUUM.

We shall now see
how Minkowski* put Einstein's results
in a remarkably neat mathematical form,
and how Einstein then utilized this
in the further application of his
Principle of Relativity,
which led to
The General Theory of Relativity,
resulting in a
NEW LAW OF GRAVITATION
and leading to further important consequences
and NEW discoveries.

It is now clear
from the Lorentz transformation (p. 19)
that
a length measurement, x' ,
in one coordinate system
depends upon BOTH x and t in another,
and that
t' also depends upon BOTH x and t.
Hence,
instead of regarding the universe
as being made up of
Space, on the one hand,
and Time, quite independent of Space,
there is a closer connection
between Space and Time
than we had realized.
In other words,

*See collection of papers mentioned in
footnote on p. 5.

that the universe is NOT a universe of points,
with time flowing along
irrespective of the points,
but rather,
this is
A UNIVERSE OF EVENTS, —
everything that happens,
happens at a certain place
AND at a certain time.

Thus, every event is characterized
by the PLACE and TIME of its occurrence.

Now,
since its place may be designated
by three numbers,
namely,
By the x, y, and z co-ordinates of the place
(using any convenient reference system),
and since the time of the event
needs only one number to characterize it,
we need in all
FOUR NUMBERS
TO CHARACTERIZE AN EVENT,
just as we need
three numbers to characterize
a point in space.

Thus we may say that
we live in a
four-dimensional world.
This does NOT mean
that we live in four-dimensional Space,
but is only another way of saying
that we live in
A WORLD OF EVENTS
rather than of POINTS only,
and it takes

FOUR numbers to designate
each significant element,
namely, each event.

Now if an event is designated
by the four numbers x, y, z, t,
in a given coordinate system,
the Lorentz transformation (p. 19)
shows how to find
the coordinates x', y', z', t',
of the same event,
in another coordinate system,
moving relatively to the first
with uniform velocity.

In studying "graphs"
every high school freshman learns
how to represent a point
by two coordinates, x and y,
using the Cartesian system of coordinates,
that is,
two straight lines
perpendicular to each other.
Now, we may also use
another pair of perpendicular axes,
X' and Y' (in the figure on the next page),
having the same origin, 0, as before,
and designate the same point by x' and y'
in this new coordinate system.
When the high school boy above-mentioned
goes to college,
and studies analytical geometry,
he then learns how to find

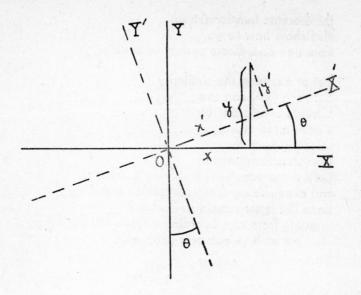

the relationship between
the primed coordinates
and the original ones,
and finds this to be expressed as follows:*

$$\left.\begin{array}{l} x = x'\cos\theta - y'\sin\theta \\ y = x'\sin\theta + y'\cos\theta \end{array}\right\}$$ (20)

and

where θ is the angle through which
the axes have been revolved,
as shown in the figure above.

The equations (20) remind one somewhat
of the Lorentz transformation (p. 19),
since the equations of

*See p. 310.

the Lorentz transformation
also show how to go
from one coordinate system to another.

Let us examine the similarity
between (20) and the
Lorentz transformation
a little more closely,
selecting from the
Lorentz transformation
only those equations involving x and t,
and disregarding those containing y and z,
since the latter remain unchanged
in going from one coordinate system to the other.
Thus we wish to compare (20) with:

$$\begin{cases} x' = \beta(x - vt) \\ t' = \beta(t - vx/c^2). \end{cases}$$

Or, if, for simplicity, we take $c = 1$,
that is, taking
the distance traveled by light in one second,
as the unit of distance,
we may say that
we wish to compare (20) with

$$\left. \begin{array}{l} x' = \beta(x - vt) \\ t' = \beta(t - vx) \end{array} \right\}. \qquad (21)$$

Let us first solve (21) for x and t,
so as to get them more nearly
in the form of (20).
By ordinary algebraic operations,*

*And remembering that
we are taking $c = 1$,
and that therefore
$$\beta = \frac{1}{\sqrt{1 - v^2}}$$

we get

$$x = \beta(x' + vt') \left.\right\}$$
and $\quad\quad t = \beta(t' + vx') \left.\right\} \;.$ $\qquad\qquad$ (22)

Before we go any further,
let us linger a moment
and consider equations (22):
Whereas (21) represents K speaking,
and saying to K':
"Now you must divide x' by β,
before you can get the relationship
between x and x' that you expect,
namely, equation (3) on p. 16;
in other words, your x' has shrunk
although you don't know it."

In (22),
it is K' speaking,
and he tells K the same thing,
namely that K must divide x by β,
to get the "true" x,
which is equal to $x' + vt'$.
Indeed,
this is quite in accord
with the discussion in Chapter VI.,
in which it was shown that
each observer
gives the other one
precisely the same advice!
Note that the only difference
between (21) and (22) is that

$$+ v \text{ becomes } - v$$

in going from one to the other.

And this is again quite in accord
with our previous discussion —
since each observer
believes himself to be at rest,
and the other fellow to be in motion,
only that one says:
"You have moved to the right" $(+ v)$,
whereas the other says:
"You have moved to the left" $(- v)$.
Otherwise,
their claims are precisely identical,
and this is exactly what
equations (21) and (22) show so clearly.

Let us now return to the comparison
of (22) and (20):
Minkowski pointed out that
if, in (22),
t is replaced by $i\tau$ (where $i = \sqrt{-1}$),
and t' by $i\tau'$,
then (22) becomes:

$$\begin{cases} x = \beta(x' + iv\tau') \\ i\tau = \beta(i\tau' + vx') \end{cases}$$

or

$$\begin{cases} x = \beta x' + i\beta v\tau' \\ i\tau = i\beta\tau' + \beta vx'. \end{cases}$$

Or (by multiplying the second equation by $-i$):

$$\begin{cases} x = \beta x' + i\beta v\tau' \\ \tau = \beta\tau' - i\beta vx'. \end{cases}$$

Finally,

Now, it will be remembered
from Euclidean plane geometry,

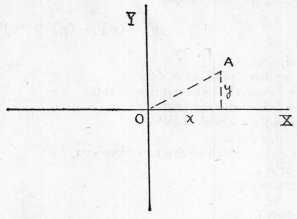

that $x^2 + y^2$ represents
the square of the distance
between O and A,
and similarly,
in Euclidean three-dimensional space,
$x^2 + y^2 + z^2$ also represents
the square of the distance between two points.
Thus, also,
$x^2 + y^2 + z^2 + \tau^2$ represents
the square of the "interval" between two EVENTS,
in our four-dimensional world (see p. 58).
And,
just as in plane geometry
the distance between two points
remains the same
whether we use
the primed or the unprimed
coordinate systems (see p. 61),
that is,

$$x^2 + y^2 = (x')^2 + (y')^2$$

67

(although x does NOT equal x',
and y does NOT equal y').
So, in three dimensions,

$$x^2 + y^2 + z^2 = (x')^2 + (y')^2 + (z')^2$$

and, similarly,
as we have seen on p. 66,
the "interval" between two events,
in our four-dimensional
space-time world of events,
remains the same,
no matter which of the two observers,
K or K',
measures it.

That is to say,
although K and K'
do not agree on some things,
as, for example,
their length and time measurements,
they DO agree on other things:

(1) The statement of their LAWS (see p. 51)
(2) The "interval" between events,
Etc.

In other words,
although length and time
are no longer INVARIANTS,
in the Einstein theory,
other quantities,
like the space-time interval between two events,
ARE invariants
in this theory.

These invariants are the quantities

68

which have the SAME value
for all observers,*
and may therefore be regarded
as the realities of the universe.

Thus, from this point of view,
NOT the things that we see or measure
are the realities,
since various observers
do not get the same measurements
of the same objects,
but rather
certain mathematical relationships
between the measurements
(Like $x^2 + y^2 + z^2 + \tau^2$)
are the realities,
since they are the same
for all observers.*

We shall see,
in discussing
The General Theory of Relativity,
how fruitful
Minkowski's view-point of a
four-dimensional Space-Time World
proved to be.

VIII. SOME CONSEQUENCES OF THE THEORY OF RELATIVITY.

We have seen that
if two observers, K and K', move
relatively to each other

*All observers moving relatively to each other
with UNIFORM velocity (see p. 56).

with constant velocity,
their measurements of length and time
are different;
and, on page 29,
we promised also to show
that their measurements of mass are different.
In this chapter we shall discuss
mass measurements,
as well as other measurements which
depend upon
these fundamental ones.

We already know that if an object moves
in a direction parallel to
the relative motion of K and K',
then the Lorentz transformation
gives the relationship
between the length and time measurements
of K and K'.

We also know that
in a direction PERPENDICULAR to
the relative motion of K and K'
there is NO difference in the
LENGTH measurements (See footnote on p. 50),
and, in this case,
the relationship between the time measurements
may be found as follows:

For this PERPENDICULAR direction
Michelson argued that
the time would be

$$t_2 = 2a\beta/c \quad \text{(see p. 12).}$$

Now this argument
is supposed to be from the point of view
of an observer who
DOES take the motion into account,

and hence already contains
the "correction" factor β;
hence,
replacing t_2 by t',
the expression $t' = 2a\beta/c$
represents the time
in the perpendicular direction
as K tells K' it SHOULD be written.
Whereas K, in his own system,
would, of course, write

$$t = 2a/c$$

for his "true" time, t.

Therefore

$$t' = \beta t$$

gives the relationship sought above,
from the point of view of K.

From this we see that
a body moving with velocity u
in this PERPENDICULAR direction,
will appear to K and K' to have
different velocities:
Thus,
Since $u = d/t$ and $u' = d'/t'$
where d and d' represent
the distance traversed by the object
as measured by K and K', respectively;
and since $d = d'$
(there being NO difference in
LENGTH measurements in this direction —
see p. 70)
and $t' = \beta t$, as shown above,
then $u' = d/\beta t = (1/\beta)u$.

Similarly,
since $a = u/t$ and $a' = u'/t'$

71

where a and a′ are the
accelerations of the body,
as measured by K and K', respectively,
we find that

$$a' = (1/\beta^2)a.$$

In like manner
we may find the relationships
between various quantities in the
primed and unprimed systems of co-ordinates,
provided they depend upon
length and time.

But, since there are THREE basic units in Physics
and since the Lorentz transformation
deals with only two of them, length and time,
the question now is
how to get the MASS into the game.
Einstein found that the best approach
to this difficult problem was via the
Conservation Laws of Classical Physics.
Then, just as the old concept of
the distance between two points
(three-dimensional)
was "stepped up" to the new one of
the interval between two events
(four-dimensional), (see p. 67)
so also the Conservation Laws
will have to be "stepped up" into
FOUR-DIMENSIONAL SPACE-TIME.
And, when this is done
an amazing vista will come into view!

CONSERVATION LAWS OF CLASSICAL PHYSICS:

(1) Conservation of Mass: this means that
    no mass can be created or destroyed,

but only transformed from one kind to another.
Thus, when a piece of wood is burned,
its mass is not destroyed, for
if one weighs all the substances into which
it is transformed, together with the ash
that remains, this total weight is the
same as the weight of the original wood.
We express this mathematically thus: $\Delta\Sigma m = o$
where Σ stands for the SUM, so that Σm
is the TOTAL mass, and Δ, as usual,
stands for the "change", so that
$\Delta\Sigma m = o$ says that the change in
total mass is zero, which is the
Mass Conservation Law in very
convenient, brief, exact form!

(2) Conservation of Momentum: this says that
if there is an exchange of momentum
(the product of mass and velocity, mv)
between bodies, say, by collision, the
TOTAL momentum BEFORE collision
is the SAME
as the TOTAL after collision: $\Delta\Sigma mv = o.$

(3) Conservation of Energy: which means that
Energy cannot be created or destroyed, but
only transformed from one kind to another.
Thus, in a motor, electrical energy is
converted to mechanical energy, whereas
in a dynamo the reverse change takes place.
And if, in both cases, we take into account
the part of the energy which is
transformed into heat energy, by friction,
then the TOTAL energy
BEFORE and AFTER the transformation
is the SAME, thus: $\Delta\Sigma E = o.$
Now, a moving body has

73

KINETIC energy, expressible thus: $\frac{1}{2}mv^2$.
When two moving, ELASTIC bodies collide,
there is no loss in kinetic energy of
the whole system, so that then we have
Conservation of Kinetic Energy: $\Delta\Sigma\frac{1}{2}mv^2 = 0$
(a special case of the more general Law);
whereas, for inelastic collision, where
some of the kinetic energy is changed into
other forms, say heat, then $\Delta\Sigma\frac{1}{2}mv^2 \neq 0$.
Are you wondering what is the use of all this?
Well, by means of these Laws, the most
PRACTICAL problems can be solved,*
hence we must know what happens to them
in Relativity Physics!
You will see that they will lead to:

(a) NEW Conservation Laws for
Momentum and Energy, which are
INVARIANT under
the Lorentz transformation,
and which reduce, for small v, ‡
to the corresponding Classical Laws
(which shows why those Laws worked
so well for so long!)

(b) the IDENTIFICATION of
MASS and ENERGY!
Hence mass CAN be destroyed as such
and actually converted into energy!
Witness the ATOMIC BOMB (see p. 318).

---

* See, for example, "Mechanics for Students of Physics and
Engineering" by Crew and Smith, Macmillan Co.,
pp. 238–241
‡ Remembering that the "correction" factor, β, is equal to
$c/\sqrt{c^2 - v^2}$, you see that, when v is small relatively to
the velocity of light, c, thus making v^2 negligible, then
$\beta = 1$ and hence no "correction" is necessary.

Thus the Classical Mass Conservation Law
was only an approximation and becomes
merged into the Conservation of Energy Law!

Even without following the mathematics of
the next few pages, you can already
appreciate the revolutionary IMPORTANCE of
these results, and become imbued with
the greatest respect for the human MIND
which can create all this and
PREDICT happenings previously unknown!
Here is MAGIC for you!

Some readers may be able to understand
the following "stepping up" process now,
others may prefer to come back to it
after reading Part II of this book:

The components of the velocity vector
in Classical Physics, are:

dx/dt, dy/dt, dz/dt.

And, if we replace x, y, z by x_1, x_2, x_3,
these become, in modern compact notation:

dx_i/dt $(i = 1, 2, 3)$.

Similarly, the momentum components are:

$m \cdot dx_i/dt$ $(i = 1, 2, 3)$

so that, for n objects,
the Classical Momentum Conservation Law is:

$$\Delta \{ \sum_n m \cdot dx_i/dt \} = o \qquad (i = 1, 2, 3) \qquad (24)$$

But (24) is NOT an invariant under
the Lorentz transformation;

the corresponding vector which IS
so invariant is:

$$\Delta\{\textstyle\sum_n m \cdot dx_i/ds\} = o \qquad (i = 1, 2, 3, 4) \qquad (25)$$

where s is the interval between two events,
and it can be easily shown * that $ds = dt/\beta$,
ds being, as you know, itself invariant
under the Lorentz transformation.
Thus, in going from 3-dimensional space
and 1-dimensional absolute time
(i.e. from Classical Physics)
to 4-dimensional SPACE-TIME,
we must use s for the independent variable
instead of t.
Now let us examine (25) which is so easily
obtained from (24) when we learn to speak the
NEW LANGUAGE OF SPACE-TIME!
Consider first only the first 3 components of (25):
Then $\Delta\{\textstyle\sum_n m \cdot dx_i/ds\} = o \quad (i = 1, 2, 3) \quad (26)$
is the NEW Momentum Conservation Law,
since, for large v, it holds whereas (24) does NOT;
and, for small v, which makes $\beta = 1$ and $ds = dt$,
(26) BECOMES (24), as it should!
And now, taking the FOURTH component of (25),
namely, $m \cdot dx_4/ds$ or $mc \cdot dt/ds$ (see p. 233)
and substituting dt/β for ds,
we get $mc\beta$ which is $mc \cdot c/\sqrt{c^2 - v^2}$ or

$$mc/\sqrt{1 - v^2/c^2} \text{ or } mc(1 - v^2/c^2)^{-\frac{1}{2}}. \qquad (27)$$

Expanding, by the binomial theorem,

we get $mc\left(1 + \dfrac{1}{2} \cdot \dfrac{v^2}{c^2} + \dfrac{3}{8} \cdot \dfrac{v^4}{c^4} + \dots\right),$

* Since $ds^2 = c^2 dt^2 - (dx^2 + dy^2 + dz^2)$ (see p. 233).
dividing by dt^2 and taking $c = 1$, we get
$(ds/dt)^2 = 1 - v^2$ and $ds/dt = \sqrt{1 - v^2} = 1/\beta$

which, for small v (neglecting terms after v^2),

becomes, approximately, $mc\left(1 + \dfrac{1}{2}\dfrac{v^2}{c^2}\right)$.   (28)

And, multiplying by c, we get $mc^2 + \frac{1}{2}mv^2$.
Hence, approximately,

$$\Delta\{\textstyle\sum_{n}(mc^2 + \frac{1}{2}mv^2)\} = 0.   \qquad (29)$$

Now, if m is constant, as for elastic collision,
then $\Delta\Sigma mc^2 = 0$ and therefore also $\Delta\Sigma(\frac{1}{2}mv^2) = 0$
which is the Classical Law of the
Conservation of Kinetic Energy for
elastic collision (see p. 74);
thus (29) reduces to this Classical Law
for small v, as it should!
Furthermore, we can also see from (29) that
for INELASTIC collision, for which

$$\Delta\{\textstyle\sum_{n}\frac{1}{2}mv^2\} \neq 0 \text{ (see p. 74)}$$

hence also $\Delta\Sigma mc^2 \neq 0$ or
c being a constant, $c^2\Delta\Sigma m \neq 0$
which says that, for inelastic collision,
even when v is small,
any loss in kinetic energy is compensated for
by an increase in mass (albeit small)
a new and startling consequence for
CLASSICAL Physics itself!
Thus, from this NEW viewpoint we realize that
even in Classical Physics
the Mass of a body is NOT a constant but
varies with changes in its energy
(the amount of change in mass being
too small to be directly observed)!
Taking now (27) instead of (28), we shall
not be limited to small v;

and, multiplying by c as before,
we get $\quad \Delta\{\underset{n}{\Sigma} mc^2\beta\} = 0$ for the
NEW Conservation Law of Energy,
which, together with (25), is invariant under the
Lorentz transformation, and which,
as we saw above, reduces to
the corresponding Classical Law, for small v.
Thus the NEW expression for the ENERGY
of a body is: $E = mc^2\beta$, which,

for $v = 0$, gives $E_0 = mc^2$, $\hfill$ (30)

showing that
ENERGY and MASS are
one and the same entity
instead of being distinct, as previously thought!
Furthermore,
even a SMALL MASS, m,
is equivalent to a LARGE amount of ENERGY,
since the multiplying factor is c^2 ,
the square of the enormous velocity of light!
Thus even an atom is equivalent to
a tremendous amount of energy.
Indeed, when a method was found (see p. 318)
of splitting an atom into two parts
and since the sum of these two masses is
less than the mass of the original atom,
you can see from (30) that
this loss in mass must yield
a terrific amount of energy
(even though this process does not transform
the entire mass of the original atom into energy).
Hence the ATOMIC BOMB! (p. 318)
Although this terrible gadget has
stunned us all into the realization
of the dangers in Science,
let us not forget that

the POWER behind it
is the human MIND itself.
Let us therefore pursue our examination of
the consequences of Relativity,
the products of this REAL POWER!

In 1901 (before Relativity),
Kaufman*, experimenting with
fast moving electrons,
found that
the apparent mass of a moving electron
is greater than that of one at rest —
a result which seemed
very strange at the time!
Now, however, with the aid of (26)
we can see
that his result is perfectly intelligible,
and indeed accounts for it quantitatively!
Thus the use of ds instead of dt,
(where $ds = dt/\beta$) brings in
the necessary correction factor, β, for large v,
not via the mass but is inherent in our
NEW RELATIVITY LANGUAGE,
in which dx_i/ds replaces the idea of
velocity, dx_i/dt, and makes it
unnecessary and undesirable to think in terms of
mass depending upon velocity.
Many writers on Relativity replace
ds by dt/β in (26) and write it:

$$\Delta\{\underset{n}{\Sigma}m\beta.dx_i/dt\} = o, \text{ putting the}$$

correction on the m.
Though this of course gives

* Gesell. Wiss. Gott. Nachr., Math.-Phys., 1901 K1-2,
  p. 143, and 1902, p. 291.

the same numerical result,
it is a concession to
CLASSICAL LANGUAGE,
and Einstein himself does not like this.
He rightly prefers that since we are
learning a NEW language (Relativity)
we should think directly in that language
and not keep translating each term
into our old CLASSICAL LANGUAGE
before we "feel" its meaning.
We must learn to "feel" modern and talk modern.

Let us next examine
another consequence of
the Theory of Relativity:

When radio waves are transmitted
through an "electromagnetic field,"
an observer K may measure
the electric and magnetic forces
at any point of the field
at a given instant.
The relationship between
these electric and magnetic forces
is expressed mathematically
by the well-known Maxwell equations
(see page 311).

Now, if another observer, K',
moving relatively to K
with uniform velocity,
makes his own measurements
on the same phenomenon,
and, according to
the Principle of Relativity,
uses the same Maxwell equations
in his primed system,

it is quite easy to show* that
the electric force
is NOT an INVARIANT
for the two observers;
and similarly
the magnetic force is also
NOT AN INVARIANT
although the relationship between
the electric and magnetic forces
expressed in the
MAXWELL EQUATIONS
has the same form for
both observers;
just as, on p. 68,
though x does NOT equal x'
and y does NOT equal y'
still the formula for
the square of the distance between two points
has the same form
in both systems of coordinates.

Thus we have seen that
the SPECIAL Theory of Relativity,
which is the subject of Part I (see p. 56),
has accomplished the following:

(1) It revised the fundamental physical concepts.

(2) By the addition of
ONLY ONE NEW POSTULATE,
namely,
the extension of
the principle of relativity

* See Einstein's first paper (pp. 52 & 53) in
the book mentioned in the footnote on p. 5.

to ELECTROMAGNETIC phenomena*
(which extension was made possible
by the above-mentioned revision
of fundamental units — see p. 55),
it explained many
ISOLATED experimental results
which baffled the
pre-Einsteinian physicists:
As, for example,
the Michelson-Morley experiment,
Kaufman's experiments (p. 79),
and many others (p. 6).

(3) It led to the merging into
ONE LAW
of the two, formerly isolated, principles,
of the Conservation of Mass and
the Conservation of Energy.

In Part II
we shall see also how
the SPECIAL Theory served as a
starting point for
the GENERAL THEORY,

*The reader may ask:
"Why call this a postulate?
Is it not based on facts?"
The answer of course is that
a scientific postulate must be
BASED on facts,
but it must go further than the known facts
and hold also for
facts that are still TO BE discovered.
So that it is really only an ASSUMPTION
(a most reasonable one, to be sure
since it agrees with facts now known),
which becomes strengthened in the course of time
if it continues to agree with NEW facts
as they are discovered.

which, again,
by means of only
ONE other assumption,
led to FURTHER NEW IMPORTANT RESULTS,
results which make the theory
the widest in scope
of any physical theory.

IX. A POINT OF LOGIC AND A SUMMARY

It is interesting here
to call attention to a logical point
which is made very clear
by the Special Theory of Relativity.
In order to do this effectively
let us first list and number
certain statements, both old and new,
to which we shall then refer by NUMBER:

(1) It is impossible for an observer
   to detect his motion through space (p. 33).

(2) The velocity of light is
   independent of the motion of the source (p. 34).

(3) The old PRE-EINSTEINIAN postulate
   that time and length measurements
   are absolute,
   that is,
   are the same for all observers.

(4) Einstein's replacement of this postulate
   by the operational fact (see p. 31)
   that
   time and length measurements

are NOT absolute,
but relative to each observer.

(5) Einstein's Principle of Relativity (p. 52).

We have seen that
(1) and (2)
are contradictory IF (3) is retained
but are NOT contradictory IF
(3) is replaced by (4).   (Ch. V.)
Hence
it may NOT be true to say that
two statements MUST be
EITHER contradictory or NOT contradictory,
without specifying the ENVIRONMENT —
Thus,
in the presence of (3)
(1) and (2) ARE contradictory,
whereas,
in the presence of (4),
the very same statements (1) and (2)
are NOT contradictory.*
We may now briefly summarize
the Special Theory of Relativity:
(1), (2) and (4)
are the fundamental ideas in it,
and,
since (1) and (4) are embodied in (5),
then (2) and (5) constitute
the BASIS of the theory.

Einstein gives these two
as POSTULATES

*Similarly
   whether two statements are
   EQUIVALENT or not
   may also depend upon the environment
   (see p. 30 of "Non-Euclidean Geometry"
   by H. G. and L. R. Lieber).

from which he then deduces
the Lorentz transformation (p. 49)
which gives the relationship
between the length and time measurements†
of two observers moving relatively to each other
with uniform velocity,
and which shows that
there is an intimate connection
between space and time.

This connection was then
EMPHASIZED by Minkowski,
who showed that
the Lorentz transformation may be regarded
as a rotation in the x, τ plane
from one set of rectangular axes to another
in a four-dimensional space-time continuum
(see Chapter VII.).

†For the relationships between
   other measurements,
   see Chapter VIII.

86

THE MORAL.

1. Local, "provincial" measurements
   are not universal,
   although they may be used
   to obtain universal realities
   if compared with other systems of
   local measurements taken from
   a different viewpoint.
   By examining certain
   RELATIONSHIPS BETWEEN
   LOCAL MEASUREMENTS,
   and finding those relationships which
   remain unchanged in going from
   one local system to another,
   one may arrive at
   the INVARIANTS of our universe.

2. By emphasizing the fact that
   absolute space and time
   are pure mental fictions,
   and that the only PRACTICAL notions of time
   that man can have
   are obtainable only by some method of signals,
   the Einstein Theory shows that
   "Idealism" alone,
   that is, "a priori" thinking alone,
   cannot serve for exploring the universe.
   On the other hand,
   since actual measurements
   are local and not universal,

87

and that only certain
THEORETICAL RELATIONSHIPS
are universal,
the Einstein Theory shows also that
practical measurement alone
is also not sufficient
for exploring the universe.
In short,
a judicious combination
Of THEORY and PRACTICE,
EACH GUIDING the other —
a "dialectical materialism" —
is our most effective weapon.

PART II
THE GENERAL THEORY

A GUIDE FOR THE READER.

I. The first three chapters of Part II give
the meaning of the term
"General Relativity,"
what it undertakes to do,
and what are its basic ideas.
These are easy reading and important.

II. Chapters XIII, XIV, and XV introduce
the fundamental mathematical ideas
which will be needed —
also easy reading and important.

III. Chapters XVI to XXII build up
the actual
streamlined mathematical machinery —
not difficult, but require
the kind of
care and patience and work
that go with learning to
run any NEW machine.
The amazing POWER of this new
TENSOR CALCULUS,
and the EASE with which it is operated,
are a genuine delight!

IV. Chapters XXIII to XXVIII show how
this machine is used to derive the
NEW LAW OF GRAVITATION.
This law,
though at first complicated

behind its seeming simplicity,
is then
REALLY SIMPLIFIED.

V.   Chapters XXIX to XXXIV constitute
THE PROOF OF THE PUDDING! —
easy reading again —
and show
what the machine has accomplished.

Then there are
a SUMMARY
and
THE MORAL.

INTRODUCTION.

In Part I,
on the SPECIAL Theory,
it was shown that
two observers who
are moving relatively to each other
with UNIFORM velocity
can formulate
the laws of the universe
"WITH EQUAL RIGHT AND
  EQUAL SUCCESS,"
even though
their points of view
are different,
and their actual measurements
do not agree.

The things that appear alike
to them both
are the "FACTS" of the universe,
the INVARIANTS.
The mathematical relationships
which both agree on
are the "LAWS" of the universe.
Since man does not know
the "true laws of God,"
why should any one human viewpoint
be singled out
as more correct than any other?
And therefore
it seems most fitting
to call THOSE relationships

"THE laws,"
which are VALID from
DIFFERENT viewpoints,
taking into consideration
all experimental data
known up to the present time.

Now, it must be emphasized
that in the Special Theory,
only that change of viewpoint
was considered
which was due to
the relative UNIFORM velocity
of the different observers.
This was accomplished by
Einstein
in his first paper*
published in 1905.
Subsequently, in 1916*,
he published a second paper
in which
he GENERALIZED the idea
to include observers
moving relatively to each other
with a CHANGING velocity
(that is, with an ACCELERATION),
and that is why it is called
"the GENERAL Theory of Relativity."

It was shown in Part I
that
to make possible
even the SPECIAL case considered there,
was not an easy task,

*See "The Principle of Relativity"
 by A. Einstein and Others,
 published by Methuen & Co., London.

for it required
a fundamental change in Physics
to remove the
APPARENT CONTRADICTION
between certain
EXPERIMENTAL FACTS!
Namely,
the change from the OLD idea
that TIME is absolute
(that is,
that it is the same for all observers)
to the NEW idea that
time is measured
RELATIVELY to an observer,
just as the ordinary
space coordinates, $x, y, z,$
are measured relatively to
a particular set of axes.
This SINGLE new idea
was SUFFICIENT
to accomplish the task
undertaken in
the Special Theory.

We shall now see that
again
by the addition of
ONLY ONE more idea,
called
"THE PRINCIPLE OF EQUIVALENCE,"
Einstein made possible
the GENERAL Theory.

Perhaps the reader may ask
why the emphasis on the fact that
ONLY ONE new idea
was added?
Are not ideas good things?

97

And is it not desirable
to have as many of them as possible?
To which the answer is that
the adequateness
of a new scientific theory
is judged

(a) By its correctness, of course,
    and
(b) By its SIMPLICITY.

No doubt everyone appreciates
the need for correctness,
but perhaps
the lay reader may not realize
the great importance of
SIMPLICITY!

"But," he will say,
"surely the Einstein Theory
is anything but simple!
Has it not the reputation
of being unintelligible
to all but a very few experts?"

Of course
"SIMPLE" does not necessarily mean
"simple to everyone," *
but only in the sense that

*Indeed, it can even be simple to
  everyone WHO
  will take the trouble to learn some
  mathematics.
  Though this mathematics
  was DEVELOPED by experts,
  it can be UNDERSTOOD by
  any earnest student.
  Perhaps even the lay reader
  will appreciate this
  after reading this little book.

98

if all known physical facts
are taken into consideration,
the Einstein Theory accounts for
a large number of these facts
in the SIMPLEST known way.

Let us now see
what is meant by
"The Principle of Equivalence,"
and what it accomplishes.

It is impossible to refrain
from the temptation
to brag about it a bit
in anticipation!
And to say that
by making the General Theory possible,
Einstein derived
A NEW LAW OF GRAVITATION
which is even more adequate than
the Newtonian one,
since it explains,
QUITE INCIDENTALLY,
experimental facts
which were left unexplained
by the older theory,
and which had troubled
the astronomers
for a long time.

And, furthermore,
the General Theory
PREDICTED NEW FACTS,
which have since been verified —
this is of course
the supreme test of any theory.

But let us get to work
to show all this.

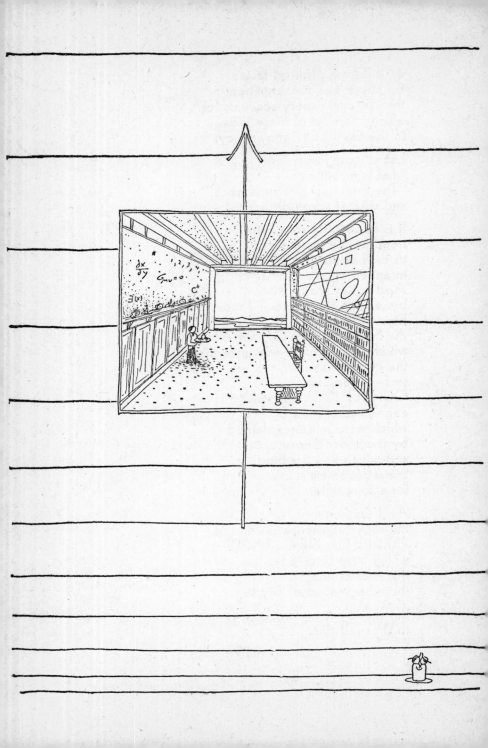

XI. THE PRINCIPLE OF EQUIVALENCE.

Consider the following situation:

Suppose that a man, Mr. *K*,
lives in a spacious box,
away from the earth
and from all other bodies,
so that there is no force of gravity
there.
And suppose that
the box and all its contents
are moving (in the direction
indicated in the drawing on p. 100)
with a changing velocity,
increasing 32 ft. per second
every second.
Now Mr. *K*,
who cannot look outside of the box,
does not know all this;
but, being an intelligent man,
he proceeds to study the behavior
of things around him.

We watch him from the outside,
but he cannot see us.

We notice that
he has a tray in his hands.
And of course we know that
the tray shares the motion of
everything in the box,

101

and therefore remains
relatively at rest to him —
namely, in his hands.
But he does not think of it in
this way;
to him, everything is actually
at rest.

Suddenly he lets go the tray.
Now we know that the tray will
continue to move upward with
CONSTANT velocity;*
and, since we also know that the box
is moving upwards with
an ACCELERATION,
we expect that very soon the floor
will catch up with the tray
and hit it.
And, of course, we see this
actually happen.
Mr. K also sees it happen,
but explains it differently, —
he says that everything was still
until he let go the tray,
and then the tray FELL and
hit the floor;
and K attributes this to
"A force of gravity."
Now K begins to study this "force."
He finds that there is an attraction
between every two bodies,

*Any moving object CONTINUES to move
with CONSTANT speed in a
STRAIGHT LINE, due to inertia,
unless it is stopped by
some external force,
like friction, for example.

and its strength is proportional to
their "gravitational masses,"
and varies inversely as the
square of the distance between them.

He also makes other experiments,
studying the behavior of bodies
pulled along a smooth table top,
and finds that different bodies offer
different degrees of resistance to
this pull,
and he concludes that the resistance
is proportional to the
"inertial mass" of a body.

And then he finds that
ANY object which he releases
FALLS with the SAME acceleration,
and therefore decides that
the gravitational mass and
the inertial mass of a body
are proportional to each other.

In other words, he explains the fact
that all bodies fall with the
SAME acceleration,
by saying that the force of gravity
is such that
the greater the resistance to motion
which a body has,
the harder gravity pulls it,
and indeed this increased pull
is supposed to be
JUST BIG ENOUGH TO OVERCOME
the larger resistance,
and thus produce
THE SAME ACCELERATION IN ALL BODIES!
Now, if Mr. *K* is a very intelligent

Newtonian physicist,
he says,
"How strange that these two distinct
properties of a body should
always be exactly proportional
to each other.
But experimental facts show
this accident to be true,
and experiments cannot be denied."
But it continues to worry him.

On the other hand,
if K is an Einsteinian relativist,
he reasons entirely differently:
"There is nothing absolute about
my way of looking at phenomena.
Mr. K', outside,
(he means us),
may see this entire room moving
upward with an acceleration,
and attribute all these happenings
to this motion
rather than to
a force of gravity
as I am doing.
His explanation and mine
are equally good,
from our different viewpoints."

This is what Einstein called
the Principle of Equivalence.

Relativist K continues:
"let me try to see things from
the viewpoint of
my good neighbor, K',
though I have never met him.
He would of course see

the floor of this room come up and
hit ANY object which I might release,
and it would therefore seem
ENTIRELY NATURAL to him
for all objects released
from a given height
at a given time
to reach the floor together,
which of course is actually the case.
Thus, instead of finding out by
long and careful EXPERIMENTATION
that
the gravitational and inertial masses
are proportional,
as my Newtonian ancestors did,
he would predict A PRIORI
that this MUST be the case.
And so,
although the facts are explainable
in either way,
K''s point of view is
the simpler one,
and throws light on happenings which
I could acquire only by
arduous experimentation, —
if I were not a relativist and hence
quite accustomed to give
equal weight to
my neighbor's viewpoint!"

Of course as we have told the story,
we know that K' is really right:
But remember that
in the actual world
we do not have this advantage:
We cannot "know" which of the two
explanations is "really" correct.

But, since they are EQUIVALENT,
we may select the simpler one,
as Einstein did.

Thus we already see
an advantage in
Einstein's Principle of Equivalence.
And,
as we said in Chapter X.
this is only the beginning,
for it led to his
new Law of Gravitation which
RETAINED ALL THE MERITS OF
NEWTON'S LAW,
and
has additional NEW merits which
Newton's Law did not have.

As we shall see.

XII. A NON-EUCLIDEAN WORLD.

Granting, then,
the Principle of Equivalence,
according to which Mr. K may replace
the idea of a "force of gravity" by
a "fictitious force" due to motion,*
the next question is:
"How does this help us to derive
A new Law of Gravitation?"
In answer to which
we ask the reader to recall
a few simple things which
he learned in elementary physics in
high school:

*The idea of a "fictitious force"
   due to motion
   is familiar to everyone
   in the following example:
   Any youngster knows that
   if he swings a pail full of water
   in a vertical plane
   WITH SUFFICIENT SPEED,
   the water will not fall out of the pail,
   even when the pail is
   actually upside down!
   And he knows that
   the centrifugal "force"
   is due to the motion only;
   since,
   if he slows down the motion,
   the water WILL fall out
   and give him a good dousing.

If a force acts on a moving object
at an angle to this motion,
it will change the course of the object,
and we say that
the body has acquired an
ACCELERATION,
even though its speed may have
remained unchanged!
This can best be seen with the aid of
the following diagram:

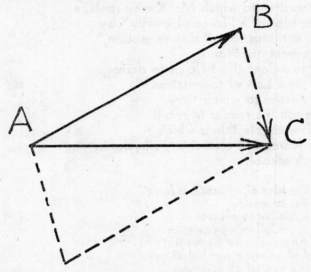

If *AB* represents the original velocity
(both in magnitude and direction)
and if the next second
the object is moving with a velocity
represented by *AC* ,
due to the fact that
some force (like the wind)
pulled it out of its course,
then obviously

BC must be the velocity which
had to be "added" to *AB*
to give the "resultant" *AC*,
as any aviator, or even
any high school boy, knows from
the "Parallelogram of forces."
Thus *BC* is the difference between
the two velocities, *AC* and *AB*.
And, since
ACCELERATION is defined as
the change in velocity, each second,
then *BC* is the acceleration,
even if *AB* and *AC* happen to be
equal in length, —
that is,
even if the speed of the object
has remained unchanged;*
the very fact that it has merely
changed in DIRECTION
shows that there is an ACCELERATION!
Thus,
if an object moves in a circle,
with uniform speed,
it is moving with
an acceleration since
it is always changing its direction.

Now imagine a physicist who
lives on a disc which
is revolving with constant speed!
Being a physicist,
he is naturally curious about the world,
and wishes to study it,
even as you and I.
And, even though we tell him that

*This distinction between "speed" and "velocity"
  is discussed on page 128.

109

he is moving with an acceleration,
he, being a democrat and a relativist,
insists that he can formulate
the laws of the universe
"WITH EQUAL RIGHT AND
EQUAL SUCCESS":
and therefore claims that
he is not moving at all
but is merely in an environment in which
a "force of gravity" is acting
(Have you ever been on a revolving disc
and actually felt this "force"?!).

Let us now watch him
tackle a problem:
We see him become interested in circles:
He wants to know whether
the circumferences of two circles
are in the same ratio as their radii.
He draws two circles,
a large one and a small one
(concentric with
the axis of revolution of the disc)
and proceeds to measure
their radii and circumferences.
When he measures the larger circumference,
we know,
from a study of
the Special Theory of Relativity*
that he will get a different value
from the one WE should get
(not being on the revolving disc);
but this is not the case with
his measurements of the radii,
since the shrinkage in length,
described in the Special Theory,

*See Part I of this book.

takes place only
IN THE DIRECTION OF MOTION,
and not in a direction which is
PERPENDICULAR to the direction of motion
(as a radius is).
Furthermore, when he measures
the circumference of the small circle,
his value is not very different from ours
since the speed of rotation is small
around a small circle,
and the shrinkage is therefore
negligible.
And so, finally, it turns out that
he finds that the circumferences
are NOT in the same ratio as the radii!
Do we tell him that he is wrong?
that this is not according to Euclid?
and that he is a fool for trying
to study Physics on a revolving disc?
Not at all!
On the contrary,
being modern relativists, we say
"That is quite all right, neighbor,
you are probably no worse than we are,
you don't have to use Euclidean geometry if
it does not work on a revolving disc,
for now there are
non-Euclidean geometries which are
exactly what you need —
Just as we would not expect
Plane Trigonometry to work on
a large portion of the earth's surface
for which we need
Spherical Trigonometry,
in which
the angle-sum of a triangle
is NOT 180°,

as we might naively demand after
a high school course in
Euclidean plane geometry.

In short,
instead of considering the disc-world
as an accelerated system,
we can,
by the Principle of Equivalence,
regard it as a system in which
a "force of gravity" is acting,
and, from the above considerations,
we see that
in a space having such a
gravitational field
Non-Euclidean geometry,
rather than Euclidean,
is applicable.

We shall now illustrate
how the geometry of
a surface or a space may be studied.
This will lead to
the mathematical consideration of
Einstein's Law of Gravitation
and its consequences.

XIII. THE STUDY OF SPACES.

Let us consider first
the familiar Euclidean plane.
Everyone knows that
for a right triangle on such a plane
the Pythagorean theorem holds:
Namely,

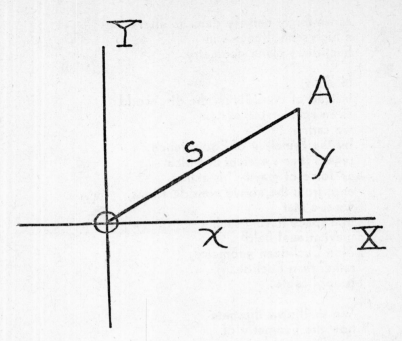

that $s^2 = x^2 + y^2$

Conversely,
it is true that
IF the distance between two points
on a surface
is given by

(1) $s^2 = x^2 + y^2$

THEN
the surface MUST BE
A EUCLIDEAN PLANE.

Furthermore,
it is obvious that
the distance from O to A
ALONG THE CURVE:

114

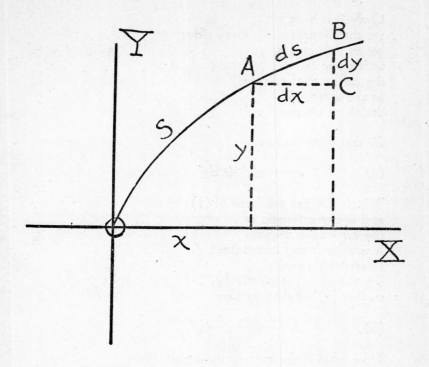

is no longer
the hypotenuse of a right triangle,
and of course
we CANNOT write here $s^2 = x^2 + y^2$!

If, however,
we take two points, A and B,
sufficiently near together,
the curve AB is so nearly
a straight line,
that we may actually regard
ABC as a little right triangle
in which the Pythagorean theorem
does hold.

Only that here
we shall represent its three sides
by ds , dx and dy ,
as is done in
the differential calculus,
to show that
the sides are small.

So that here we have

(2) $$ds^2 = dx^2 + dy^2$$

Which still has the form of (1)
and is characteristic of
the Euclidean plane.
It will be found convenient
to replace x and y
by x_1 and x_2 , respectively,
so that (2) may be written

(3) $$ds^2 = dx_1^2 + dx_2^2.$$

Now what is the corresponding situation
on a non-Euclidean surface,
such as,
the surface of a sphere, for example?

Let us take
two points on this surface, A and B ,
designating the position of each
by its latitude and longitude:

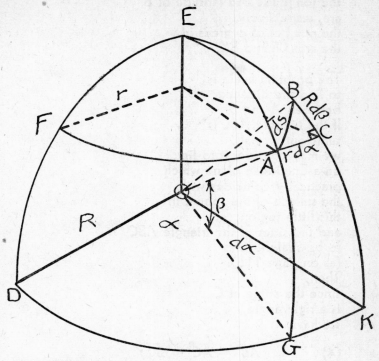

Let *DE* be the meridian
from which
longitude is measured —
the Greenwich meridian.
And let *DK* be a part of the equator,
and *E* the north pole.
Then the longitude and latitude of *A*
are, respectively,
the number of degrees in
the arcs *AF* and *AG* ,
(or in the
corresponding central angles, α and β).
Similarly,

117

the longitude and latitude of *B*
are, respectively,
the number of degrees in
the arcs *CF* and *BK*.

The problem again is
to find the distance
between *A* and *B*.
If the triangle *ABC* is
sufficiently small,
we may consider it to lie
on a Euclidean plane which
practically coincides with
the surface of the sphere in
this little region,
and the sides of the triangle *ABC*
to be straight lines
(as on page 115).
Then,
since the angle at *C*
is a right angle,
we have

(4) $$\overline{AB}^2 = \overline{AC}^2 + \overline{BC}^2.$$

And now let us see
what this expression becomes
if we change
the Cartesian coordinates in (4)
(in the tangent Euclidean plane)
to the coordinates known as
longitude and latitude
on the surface of the sphere.

Obviously *AB*
has a perfectly definite length
irrespective of

118

which coordinate system we use;
but AC and BC ,
the Cartesian coordinates in
the tangent Euclidean plane
may be transformed into
longitude and latitude on
the surface of the sphere, thus:
let r be
the radius of the latitude circle FAC ,
and R the radius of the sphere.
Then

$$AC = r \cdot d\alpha.*$$

Similarly
$$BC = R \cdot d\beta.$$

Therefore, substituting in (4),
we have

(5) $$ds^2 = r^2 d\alpha^2 + R^2 d\beta^2.$$

And, replacing α by x_1 , and β by x_2 ,
this may be written

(6) $$ds^2 = r^2 dx_1^2 + R^2 dx_2^2 .$$

A comparison of (6) and (3)
will show that

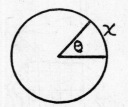

*any high school student knows
that if x represents the length of
an arc, and θ is the number of
radians in it, then

$$x/\theta = 2\pi r/2\pi$$

And therefore

$$x = r\theta.$$

120

on the sphere,
the expression for ds^2
is not quite so simple
as it was on the Euclidean plane.

The question naturally arises,
does this distinction between
a Euclidean and a non-Euclidean surface
always hold,
and is this a way
to distinguish between them?

That is,
if we know
the algebraic expression which represents
the distance between two points
which actually holds
on a given surface,
can we then immediately decide
whether the surface
is Euclidean or not?
Or does it perhaps depend upon
the coordinate system used?

To answer this,
let us go back to the Euclidean plane,
and use oblique coordinates
instead of the more familiar
rectangular ones
thus:

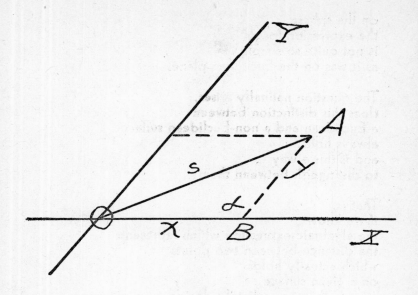

The coordinates of the point A
are now represented by
x and y
which are measured
parallel to the X and Y axes,
and are now
NOT at right angles to each other.

Can we now find
the distance between O and A
using these oblique coordinates?
Of course we can,
for,
by the well-known
Law of Cosines in Trigonometry,
we can represent
the length of a side of a triangle

122

lying opposite an obtuse angle,
by:

$$s^2 = x^2 + y^2 - 2xy \cos \alpha.$$

Or, for a very small triangle,

$$ds^2 = dx^2 + dy^2 - 2dxdy \cos \alpha.$$

And, if we again
replace x and y
by x_1 and x_2 , respectively,
this becomes

(7) $$ds^2 = dx_1^2 + dx_2^2 - 2\, dx_1 \cdot dx_2 \cdot \cos \alpha.$$

Here we see that
even on a Euclidean plane,
the expression for ds^2
is not as simple as it was before.

And, if we had used
polar coordinates
on a Euclidean plane,
we would have obtained

$$ds^2 = dr^2 + r^2 d\theta^2 \;*$$

or

(8) $$ds^2 = dx_1^2 + x_1^2 dx_2^2. \;*$$

* (See page 124)

The reader should verify this,
remembering that
the polar coordinates of point P

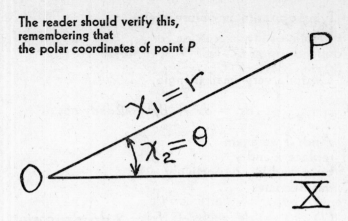

are
(1) its distance, x_1, from a fixed point, O,
(2) the angle, x_2, which OP makes with a fixed line OX.
Then (8) is obvious from
the following figure:

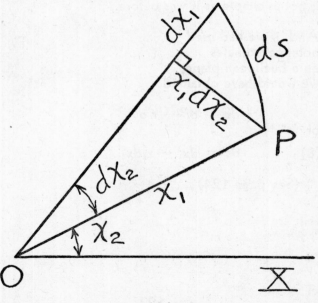

124

Hence we see that
the form of the expression for ds^2
depends upon BOTH
(a) the KIND OF SURFACE
we are dealing with,
and
(b) the particular
COORDINATE SYSTEM.

We shall soon see that
whereas
a mere superficial inspection
of the expression for ds^2
is not sufficient
to determine the kind of surface
we are dealing with,
a DEEPER examination
of this expression
DOES help us to know this.
For this deeper examination
we must know
how,
from the expression for ds^2,
to find
the so-called "CURVATURE TENSOR"
of the surface.

And this brings us to
the study of tensors:

What are tensors?
Of what use are they?
and HOW are they used?

Let us see.

XIV. WHAT IS A TENSOR?

The reader is no doubt familiar
with the words "scalar" and "vector."
A scalar is a quantity which
has magnitude only,
whereas
a vector has
both magnitude and direction.

Thus,
if we say that
the temperature at a certain place
is 70° Fahrenheit,
there is obviously NO DIRECTION
to this temperature,
and hence
TEMPERATURE is a SCALAR.
But
if we say that
an airplane has gone
one hundred miles east,
obviously its displacement
from its original position
is a VECTOR,
whose MAGNITUDE is 100 miles,
and whose DIRECTION is EAST.

Similarly,
a person's AGE is a SCALAR,
whereas

the VELOCITY with which an object moves
is a VECTOR,*
and so on;
the reader can easily
find further examples
of both scalars and vectors.

We shall now discuss
some quantities
which come up in our experience
and which are
neither scalars nor vectors,
but which are called
TENSORS.
And,
when we have illustrated and defined these,
we shall find that
a SCALAR is a TENSOR whose RANK is ZERO,
and
a VECTOR is a TENSOR whose RANK is ONE,
and we shall see what is meant by
a TENSOR of RANK TWO, or THREE, etc.
Thus "TENSOR" is a more inclusive term,

*A distinction is often made between
"speed" and "velocity"—
the former is a SCALAR, the latter a VECTOR.
Thus when we are interested ONLY in
HOW FAST a thing is moving,
and do not care about its
DIRECTION of motion,
we must then speak of its SPEED,
but if we are interested ALSO in its
DIRECTION,
we must speak of its VELOCITY.
Thus the SPEED of an automobile
would be designated by
"Thirty miles an hour,"
but its VELOCITY would be
"Thirty miles an hour EAST."

of which "SCALAR" and "VECTOR" are
SPECIAL CASES.

Before we discuss
the physical meaning of
a tensor of rank two,
let us consider
the following facts about vectors.

Suppose that we have
any vector, *AB* , in a plane,
and suppose that
we draw a pair of rectangular axes,
X and *Y*,
thus:

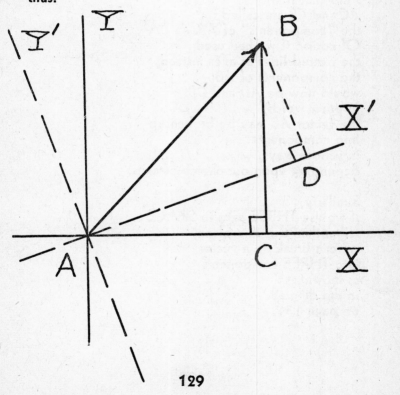

Drop a perpendicular *BC*
from *B* to the *X*-axis.
Then we may say that
AC is the *X*-component of *AB* ,
and *CB* is the *Y*-component of *AB* ;
for,
as we know from
the elementary law of
"The parallelogram of forces,"
if a force *AC* acts on a particle
and *CB* also acts on it,
the resultant effect is the same
as that of a force *AB* alone.
And that is why
AC and *CB* are called
the "components" of *AB*.
Of course if we had used
the dotted lines as axes instead,
the components of *AB*
would now be *AD* and *DB*.
In other words,
the vector *AB* may be broken up
into components
in various ways,
depending upon our choice of axes.

Similarly,
if we use THREE axes in SPACE
rather than two in a plane,
we can break up a vector
into THREE components
as shown
in the diagram
on page 131.

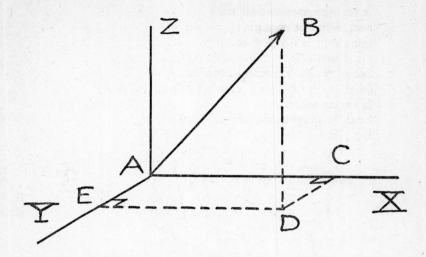

By dropping the perpendicular *BD*
from *B* to the *XY*-plane,
and then drawing
the perpendiculars *DC* and *DE*
to the *X* and *Y* axes, respectively,
we have the three components of *AB* ,
namely,
AC , *AE* and *DB* ;
and, as before,
the components depend upon
the particular choice of axes.

Let us now illustrate
the physical meaning
of a tensor of rank two.

Suppose we have a rod
at every point of which
there is a certain strain
due to some force acting on it.
As a rule the strain

131

is not the same at all points,
and, even at any given point,
the strain is not the same in
all directions.*
Now, if the STRESS at the point A
(that is, the FORCE causing the strain at A)
is represented
both in magnitude and direction
by AB

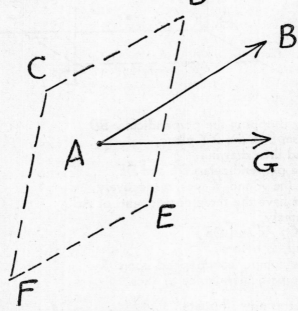

*When an object finally breaks
under a sufficiently great strain,
it does not fly into bits
as it would do if
the strain were the same
at all points and in all directions,
but breaks along certain lines
where, for one reason or another,
the strain is greatest.

and if we are interested to know
the effect of this force upon
the surface *CDEF* (through *A*),
we are obviously dealing
with a situation which depends
not on a SINGLE vector,
but on TWO vectors:
Namely,
one vector, *AB* ,
which represents the force in question,
and another vector
(call it *AG*),
whose direction will indicate
the ORIENTATION of the surface *CDEF* ,
and whose magnitude will represent
the AREA of *CDEF*.

In other words,
the effect of a force upon a surface
depends NOT ONLY on the force itself
but ALSO on the
size and orientation of the surface.

Now, how can we indicate
the orientation of a surface
by a line?
If we draw a line through *A*
in the plane *CDEF* ,
obviously we can draw this line
in many different directions,
and there is no way
of choosing one of these
to represent the orientation of this surface.
BUT,
if we take a line through *A*
PERPENDICULAR to the plane *CDEF* ,
such a line is UNIQUE

133

and CAN therefore be used
to specify the orientation
of the surface CDEF.
Hence, if we draw a vector, AG ,
in a direction perpendicular to CDEF
and of such a length that
it represents the magnitude of
the area of CDEF ,
then obviously
this vector AG
indicates clearly
both the SIZE and the ORIENTATION
of the surface CDEF.

Thus,
the STRESS at A
upon the surface CDEF
depends upon the TWO vectors,
AB and AG ,
and is called
a TENSOR of RANK TWO.

Let us now find a convenient way
of representing this tensor.
And, in order to do so,
let us consider the stress, F ,
upon a small surface, dS ,
represented in the following figure
by ABC (= dS).
Now if OG, perpendicular to ABC ,
is the vector which represents
the size and orientation of ABC ,
then,

134

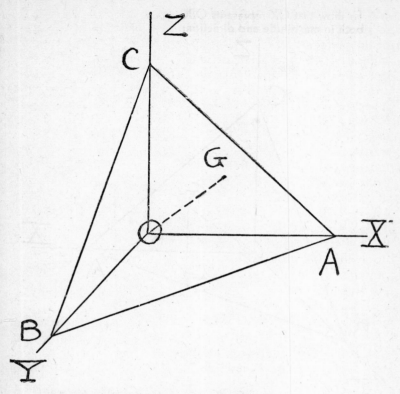

it is quite easy to see (page 136)

that the X-component of OG
represents in magnitude and direction
the projection OBC of ABC upon the YZ-plane.
And similarly,
the Y and Z components of OG
represent the projections
OAC and OAB , respectively.

135

To show that OK represents OBC
both in magnitude and direction:

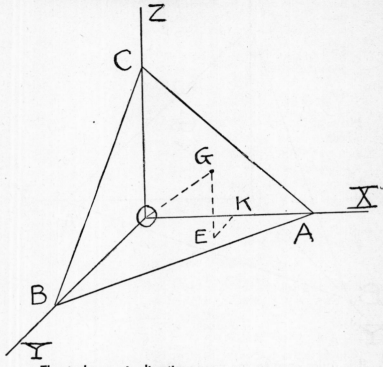

That it does so in direction
is obvious,
since OK is perpendicular to OBC (see p. 134).
As regards the magnitude
we must now show that

$$\frac{OK}{OG} = \frac{OBC}{ABC}:$$

(a) Now OBC = ABC x cos of the dihedral angle
between ABC and OBC
(since the area of the projection
of a given surface
is equal to
the area of the given surface multiplied by

the cosine of the dihedral angle
between the two planes).
But this dihedral angle equals angle GOK
since OG and OK are respectively
perpendicular to ABC and OBC,
and cos $\angle GOK$ is OK/OG.
Substitution of this in (a)
gives the required

$$\frac{OBC}{ABC} = \frac{OK}{OG}.$$

Now, if the force F,
which is itself a vector,
acts on ABC,
we can examine its total effect
by considering separately
the effects of its three components

$$f_x, f_y, \text{ and } f_z$$

upon EACH of the three projections

OBC, OAC and OAB.

Let us designate these projections
by dS_x, dS_y and dS_z, respectively.

Now,
since f_x
(which is the X-component of F)
acts upon EACH one of the three
above-mentioned projections,
let us designate the pressure
due to this component alone
upon the three projections
by

$$p_{xx}, p_{xy}, p_{xz},$$

respectively.

We must emphasize
the significance of this notation:
In the first place,

137

the reader must distinguish between
the "pressure" on a surface
and the "force" acting on the surface.
The "pressure" is
the FORCE PER UNIT AREA.
So that
the TOTAL FORCE is obtained by
MULTIPLYING
the PRESSURE by the AREA of the surface.
Thus the product

$$p_{xx} \cdot dS_x$$

gives the force acting upon
the projection dS_x
due to the action of f_x ALONE.
Note the DOUBLE subscripts in

$$p_{xx}, \; p_{xy}, \; p_{xz} :$$

The first one obviously refers to the fact
that
these three pressures all emanate
from the component f_x alone;
whereas,
the second subscript designates
the particular projection upon which
the pressure acts.
Thus p_{xy} means
the pressure due to f_x
upon the projection dS_y,
Etc.
It follows therefore that

$$f_x = p_{xx} \cdot dS_x + p_{xy} \cdot dS_y + p_{xz} \cdot dS_z .$$

And, similarly,

$$f_y = p_{yx} \cdot dS_x + p_{yy} \cdot dS_y + p_{yz} \cdot dS_z$$

and

$$f_z = p_{zx} \cdot dS_x + p_{zy} \cdot dS_y + p_{zz} \cdot dS_z .$$

138

Hence the TOTAL STRESS, F,
on the surface dS,
is

$$F = f_x + f_y + f_z$$

or

$$F = p_{xx} \cdot dS_x + p_{xy} \cdot dS_y + p_{xz} \cdot dS_z$$
$$+ p_{yx} \cdot dS_x + p_{yy} \cdot dS_y + p_{yz} \cdot dS_z$$
$$+ p_{zx} \cdot dS_x + p_{zy} \cdot dS_y + p_{zz} \cdot dS_z.$$

Thus we see that
stress is not just a vector,
with three components in
three-dimensional space (see p. 130)
but has NINE components
in THREE-dimensional space.
Such a quantity is called
A TENSOR OF RANK TWO.

For the present
let this illustration of a tensor suffice:
Later we shall give a precise definition.

It is obvious that
if we were dealing with a plane
instead of with
three-dimensional space,
a tensor of rank two would then have
only FOUR components instead of nine,
since each of the two vectors involved
has only two components in a plane,
and therefore,
there would now be only
2×2 components for the tensor
instead of 3×3 as above.

And, in general,
if we are dealing with
n-dimensional space,

a tensor of rank two
has n^2 components
which are therefore conveniently written
in a SQUARE array
as was done on page 139.
Whereas,
in n-dimensional space,
a VECTOR has only n components:
Thus,
a VECTOR in a PLANE
has TWO components;
in THREE-dimensional space it has
THREE components;
and so on.

Hence,
the components of a VECTOR
are therefore written
in a SINGLE ROW;
instead of in a SQUARE ARRAY
as in the case of a TENSOR of RANK TWO.

Similarly,
in n-dimensional space
a TENSOR of rank THREE has n^3 components,
and so on.

To sum up:

In n-dimensional space,
a VECTOR has n components,
a TENSOR of rank TWO has n^2 components,
a TENSOR of rank THREE has n^3 components,
and so on.

The importance of tensors
in Relativity
will become clear
as we go on.

140

XV. THE EFFECT ON TENSORS OF A CHANGE IN THE COORDINATE SYSTEM.

In Part I of this book (page 61)
we had occasion to mention
the fact that
the coordinates of the point A

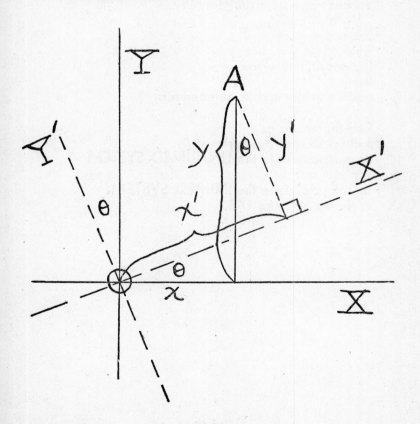

in the unprimed coordinate system
can be expressed in terms of
its coordinates in the
primed coordinate system
by the relationships

$$(9) \qquad \begin{cases} x = x' \cos\theta - y' \sin\theta \\ y = x' \sin\theta + y' \cos\theta \end{cases}$$

as is known to any young student of
elementary analytical geometry.

Let us now see
what effect this change in
the coordinate system
has
upon a vector and its components.

Call the vector ds,
and let dx and dy represent
its components in the UNPRIMED SYSTEM,
and dx' and dy'
its components in the PRIMED SYSTEM
as shown on page 143.

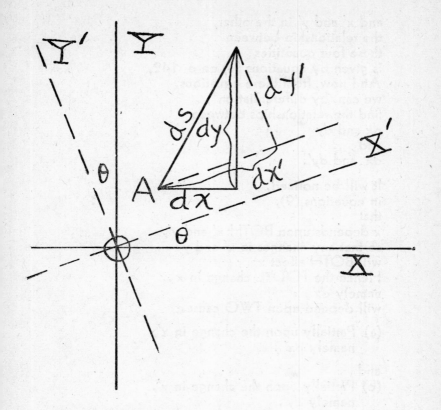

Obviously ds itself
is not affected by the change
of coordinate system,
but the COMPONENTS of ds
in the two systems
are DIFFERENT,
as we have already pointed out
on page 130.

Now if the coordinates of point A
are x and y in one system

143

and x' and y' in the other,
the relationship between
these four quantities
is given by equations (9) on p. 142.
And now, from these equations,
we can, by differentiation*,
find the relationships between
dx and dy
and
dx' and dy'.

It will be noticed,
in equations (9),
that
x depends upon BOTH x' and y',
so that any changes in x' and y'
will BOTH affect x.
Hence the TOTAL change in x,
namely dx,
will depend upon TWO causes:

(a) Partially upon the change in x',
    namely dx',

and

(b) Partially upon the change in y',
    namely dy'.

Before writing out these changes,
it will be found more convenient
to solve (9) for x' and y'
in terms of x and y.†

*See any book on
  Differential Calculus.
†Assuming of course that the
  determinant of the coefficients in (9)
  is not zero.
  (See the chapter on "Determinants" in
  "Higher Algebra" by M. Bocher.)

In other words,
to express the
NEW, primed coordinates, x' and y',
in terms of the
OLD, original ones, x and y,
rather than the other way around.

This will of course give us

(10) $\begin{cases} x' = ax + by \\ y' = cx + dy \end{cases}$

where a, b, c, d are functions of θ.

It will be even better
to write (10) in the form:

(11) $\begin{cases} x_1' = a_{11}x_1 + a_{12}x_2 \\ x_2' = a_{21}x_1 + a_{22}x_2 \end{cases}$

using x_1 and x_2 instead of x and y,
(and of course x_1' and x_2' instead of
x' and y');
and putting different subscripts
on the single letter a,
instead of using
four different letters: a, b, c, d.
The advantage of this notation is
not only that we can
easily GENERALIZE to n dimensions
from the above
two-dimensional statements,
but,
as we shall see later,
this notation lends itself to
a beautifully CONDENSED way of
writing equations,
which renders them
very EASY to work with.

145

Let us now proceed with
the differentiation of (11):
we get

(12)
$$\begin{cases} dx_1' = a_{11}dx_1 + a_{12}dx_2 \\ dx_2' = a_{21}dx_1 + a_{22}dx_2 \end{cases}$$

The MEANING of the a's in (12)
should be clearly understood:
Thus a_{11} is
the change in x_1' due to
A UNIT CHANGE in x_1,
so that
when it is multiplied by
the total change in x_1, namely dx_1,
we get
THE CHANGE IN x_1' DUE TO
THE CHANGE IN x_1 ALONE.
And similarly in $a_{12}dx_2$,
a_{12} represents
the change in x_1' PER UNIT CHANGE in x_2,
and therefore
the product of a_{12} and
the total change in x_2, namely dx_2,
gives
THE CHANGE IN x_1' DUE TO
THE CHANGE IN x_2 ALONE.

Thus
the TOTAL CHANGE in x_1'
is given by
$$a_{11}dx_1 + a_{12}dx_2,$$
just as
the total cost of
a number of apples and oranges
would be found
by multiplying the cost of
ONE APPLE
by the total number of apples,

146

and ADDING this result
to a similar one
for the oranges.

And similarly for dx_2' in (12).

We may therefore
replace a_{11} by $\partial x_1'/\partial x_1$
a symbol which represents
the partial change in x_1'
per unit change in x_1*,
and is called
the "partial derivative of x_1'
with respect to x_1 ."

Similarly,

$$a_{12} = \frac{\partial x_1'}{\partial x_2}, \quad a_{21} = \frac{\partial x_2'}{\partial x_1}, \quad a_{22} = \frac{\partial x_2'}{\partial x_2}.$$

And we may therefore rewrite (12)
in the form

(13)
$$\begin{cases} dx_1' = \dfrac{\partial x_1'}{\partial x_1} \cdot dx_1 + \dfrac{\partial x_1'}{\partial x_2} \cdot dx_2 \\[3mm] dx_2' = \dfrac{\partial x_2'}{\partial x_1} \cdot dx_1 + \dfrac{\partial x_2'}{\partial x_2} \cdot dx_2 \end{cases}$$

But perhaps the reader
is getting a little tired of all this,
and is wondering
what it has to do
with Relativity.

*Note that a PARTIAL change
is always denoted by the letter "∂"
in contrast to "d"
which designates a TOTAL change

To which we may give him
a partial answer now
and hold out hope
of further information
in the remaining chapters.
What we can already say is that
since General Relativity is concerned with
finding the laws of the physical world
which hold good for ALL observers,*
and since various observers
differ from each other,
as physicists,
only in that they
use different coordinate systems,
we see then
that Relativity is concerned
with finding out those things
which remain INVARIANT
under transformations of
coordinate systems.

Now, as we saw on page 143,
a vector is such an INVARIANT;
and, similarly,
tensors in general
are such INVARIANTS,
so that the business of the physicist
really becomes
to find out
which physical quantities
are tensors,
and are therefore
the "facts of the universe,"
since they hold good
for all observers.

*See p. 96.

Besides,
as we promised on page 125,
we must explain the meaning of
"curvature tensor,"
since it is this tensor
which CHARACTERIZES a space.

And then
with the aid of the curvature tensor of
our four-dimensional world of events,*
we shall find out
how things move in this world —
what paths the planets take,
and in what path
a ray of light travels
as it passes near the sun,
and so on.

And of course
these are all things which
can be
VERIFIED BY EXPERIMENT.

XVI. A VERY HELPFUL SIMPLIFICATION

Before we go any further
let us write equations (13) on page 147
more briefly
thus:

$$(14) \qquad dx'_\mu = \Sigma_\sigma \frac{\partial x'_\mu}{\partial x_\sigma} \cdot dx_\sigma \qquad \left(\begin{matrix} \mu = 1 , 2. \\ \sigma = 1 , 2. \end{matrix} \right)$$

*FOUR-dimensional, since
each event is characterized by
its THREE space-coordinates and
the TIME of its occurrence
(see Part I. of this book, page 58)

A careful study of (14) will show

(a) That (14) really contains TWO equations

(although it looks like only one),
since, as we give μ
its possible values, 1 and 2 ,
we have
dx_1' and dx_2' on the left,
just as we did in (13);

(b) The symbol Σ_σ means that
when the various values of σ ,
namely 1 and 2 ,
are substituted for σ
(keeping the μ constant in any one equation)
the resulting two terms
must be ADDED together.
Thus, for $\mu = 1$ and $\sigma = 1 , 2 ,$
(14) becomes

$$dx_1' = \frac{\partial x_1'}{\partial x_1} \cdot dx_1 + \frac{\partial x_1'}{\partial x_2} \cdot dx_2 ,$$

just like the FIRST equation in (13),
and, similarly,
by taking $\mu = 2$,
and again "summing on the σ's ,"
since that is what Σ_σ tells us to do,
we get

$$dx_2' = \frac{\partial x_2'}{\partial x_1} \cdot dx_1 + \frac{\partial x_2'}{\partial x_2} \cdot dx_2 ,$$

which is the SECOND equation in (13).
Thus we see that
(14) includes all of (13).

A still further abbreviation
is introduced by omitting
the symbol Σ_σ

151

WITH THE UNDERSTANDING THAT
WHENEVER A SUBSCRIPT OCCURS TWICE
IN A SINGLE TERM
(as, for example, σ
in the right-hand member of (14)),
it will be understood that
a SUMMATION is to be made
ON THAT SUBSCRIPT.
Hence we may write (14) as follows:

$$(15) \qquad dx'_\mu = \frac{\partial x'_\mu}{\partial x_\sigma} \cdot dx_\sigma \qquad \left(\begin{array}{l} \mu = 1, 2 \\ \sigma = 1, 2 \end{array} \right)$$

in which we shall know
that the presence of the TWO σ's
in the term on the right,
means that Σ_σ is understood.

And now, finally,
since dx_1 and dx_2
are the components of ds in the
UNPRIMED system
let us represent them more briefly by

$$A^1 \text{ and } A^2$$

respectively.
The reader must NOT confuse
these SUPERSCRIPTS
with EXPONENTS —
thus A^2 is not the "square of" A,
but the superscript serves merely
the same purpose as a
SUBSCRIPT,
namely,
to distinguish the components
from each other.
Just why we use
SUPERSCRIPTS instead of subscripts
will appear later (p. 172).

152

And the components of *ds*
in the PRIMED coordinate system
will now be written

$$A'^1 \text{ and } A'^2.$$

Thus (15) becomes

(16) $\qquad A'^\mu = \dfrac{\partial x'_\mu}{\partial x_\sigma} \cdot A^\sigma.$

And so,
if we have a certain vector A^σ,
that is,
a vector whose components are
A^1 and A^2
in a certain coordinate system,
and if we change to
a new coordinate system
in accordance with
the transformation represented by (11) on page 145 ,
then
(16) tells us what will be
the components of this same vector
in the new (PRIMED) coordinate system.

Indeed, (15) or (16) represents
the change in the components
of a vector
NOT ONLY for the change given in (11),
but for ANY transformation
of coordinates:*
Thus
suppose x_σ are the coordinates of
a point in one coordinate system,

*Except only that
the values of (x_σ) and (x_μ') must be in
one-to-one correspondence.

154

and suppose that

$$x'_1 = f_1(x_1, x_2, \ldots) = f_1(x_\sigma)$$
$$x'_2 = f_2(x_\sigma)$$

etc.
Or, representing this entire
set of equations by

$$x'_\mu = f_\mu(x_\sigma),$$

where the f's represent
any functions whatever,
then, obviously

$$dx'_1 = \frac{\partial f_1}{\partial x_1} \cdot dx_1 + \frac{\partial f_1}{\partial x_2} \cdot dx_2 + \ldots$$

or, since $f_1 = x'_1$,

$$dx'_1 = \frac{\partial x'_1}{\partial x_1} \cdot dx_1 + \frac{\partial x'_1}{\partial x_2} \cdot dx_2 + \ldots$$

etc.
Hence

$$dx'_\mu = \frac{\partial x'_\mu}{\partial x_\sigma} \cdot dx_\sigma \text{ or } A'^\mu = \frac{\partial x'_\mu}{\partial x_\sigma} \cdot A^\sigma$$

gives the manner of transformation
of the vector dx_σ to
ANY other coordinate system
(see the only limitation
mentioned in the footnote on
page 154).

And in fact
ANY set of quantities which
transforms according to (16) is
DEFINED TO BE A VECTOR,
or rather,
A CONTRAVARIANT VECTOR —
the meaning of "CONTRAVARIANT"
155

will appear later (p. 172).
The reader must not forget that
whereas the separate components in
the two coordinate systems are
different,
the vector itself is
an INVARIANT under the
transformation of coordinates
(see page 143).
It should be noted further that
(16) serves not only to represent
a two-dimensional vector,
but may represent
a three- or four- or
n-dimensional vector,
since all that is necessary is
to indicate the number of values that
μ and σ may take.
Thus, if $\mu = 1, 2$ and $\sigma = 1, 2$,
we have a two-dimensional vector;
but if $\mu = 1, 2, 3$, and $\sigma = 1, 2, 3$,
(16) represents a 3-dimensional vector,
and so on.
For the case $\mu = 1, 2, 3$ and $\sigma = 1, 2, 3$,
(16) obviously represents
THREE EQUATIONS in which
the right-hand members
each have THREE terms:

$$A'^1 = \frac{\partial x_1'}{\partial x_1} \cdot A^1 + \frac{\partial x_1'}{\partial x_2} \cdot A^2 + \frac{\partial x_1'}{\partial x_3} \cdot A^3$$

$$A'^2 = \frac{\partial x_2'}{\partial x_1} \cdot A^1 + \frac{\partial x_2'}{\partial x_2} \cdot A^2 + \frac{\partial x_2'}{\partial x_3} \cdot A^3$$

$$A'^3 = \frac{\partial x_3'}{\partial x_1} \cdot A^1 + \frac{\partial x_3'}{\partial x_2} \cdot A^2 + \frac{\partial x_3'}{\partial x_3} \cdot A^3$$

156

Similarly we may now give
the mathematical definition of
a tensor of rank two,*
or of any other rank.
Thus
a contravariant tensor of rank two
is defined as follows:

$$\text{(17)} \qquad A'^{\alpha\beta} = \frac{\partial x'_\alpha}{\partial x_\gamma} \cdot \frac{\partial x'_\beta}{\partial x_\delta} \cdot A^{\gamma\delta}$$

Here, since γ and δ occur TWICE
in the term on the right,
it is understood that
we must SUM for these indices
over whatever range of values they have.
Thus if we are speaking of
THREE DIMENSIONAL SPACE,
we have $\gamma = 1, 2, 3$ and $\delta = 1, 2, 3$.
ALSO $\alpha = 1, 2, 3$, and $\beta = 1, 2, 3$;
But
NO SUMMATION is to be performed
on the α and β
since neither of them occurs
TWICE in a single term;
so that
any particular values of α and β
must be retained throughout ANY ONE equation.

For example,
for the case $\alpha = 1, \beta = 2$,

*It will be remembered (see page 128)
  that
   a VECTOR is a TENSOR of RANK ONE.

157

(17) gives the equation:

$$A'^{12} = \frac{\partial x_1'}{\partial x_1} \cdot \frac{\partial x_2'}{\partial x_1} \cdot A^{11} + \frac{\partial x_1'}{\partial x_1} \cdot \frac{\partial x_2'}{\partial x_2} \cdot A^{12} + \frac{\partial x_1'}{\partial x_1} \cdot \frac{\partial x_2'}{\partial x_3} \cdot A^{13}$$

$$+ \frac{\partial x_1'}{\partial x_2} \cdot \frac{\partial x_2'}{\partial x_1} \cdot A^{21} + \frac{\partial x_1'}{\partial x_2} \cdot \frac{\partial x_2'}{\partial x_2} \cdot A^{22} + \frac{\partial x_1'}{\partial x_2} \cdot \frac{\partial x_2'}{\partial x_3} \cdot A^{23}$$

$$+ \frac{\partial x_1'}{\partial x_3} \cdot \frac{\partial x_2'}{\partial x_1} \cdot A^{31} + \frac{\partial x_1'}{\partial x_3} \cdot \frac{\partial x_2'}{\partial x_2} \cdot A^{32} + \frac{\partial x_1'}{\partial x_3} \cdot \frac{\partial x_2'}{\partial x_3} \cdot A^{33}$$

It will be observed that γ and δ
have each taken on
their THREE possible values: 1 , 2 , 3 ,
which resulted in
NINE terms on the right,
whereas
$\alpha = 1$ and $\beta = 2$
have been retained throughout.

And now since α and β
may each have the three values, 1 , 2 , 3 ,
there will be
NINE such EQUATIONS in all.

Thus (17) represents
nine equations each containing
nine terms on the right,
if we are considering
three-dimensional space.
Obviously for two-dimensional space,
(17) will represent
only four equations each containing
only four terms on the right.
Whereas,
in four dimensions,
as we must have in
Relativity*

*See the footnote on p. 150.

158

(17) will represent
sixteen equations each containing
sixteen terms on the right.

And, in general,
in n-dimensional space,
a tensor of RANK TWO,
defined by (17),
consists of
n^2 equations, each containing
n^2 terms in the right-hand member.

Similarly,
a contravariant tensor of RANK THREE
is defined by

(18) $A'^{\alpha\beta\gamma} = \dfrac{\partial x'_\alpha}{\partial x_\mu} \cdot \dfrac{\partial x'_\beta}{\partial x_\nu} \cdot \dfrac{\partial x'_\gamma}{\partial x_\sigma} \cdot A^{\mu\nu\sigma}$

and so on.
As before,
the number of equations represented by (18)
and the number of terms on the right in each,
depend upon
the dimensionality of the space in question.

The reader can already appreciate somewhat
the remarkable brevity
of this notation.
But when he will see in the next chapter
how easily such sets of equations
are MANIPULATED,
he will be really delighted,
we are sure of that.

XVII. OPERATIONS WITH TENSORS.

For example,
take the vector (or tensor of rank one) A^α,
having the two components A^1 and A^2
in a plane,
with reference to a given set of axes.
And let B^α be another such vector.
Then, by adding the corresponding components
of A^α and B^α,
we obtain a quantity
also having two components,
namely,

$$A^1 + B^1 \text{ and } A^2 + B^2$$

which may be represented by

$$C^1 \text{ and } C^2,$$

respectively.

Let us now prove
that this quantity
is also a vector:
Since A^α is a vector,
its law of transformation is:

(19) $\qquad A'^\lambda = \dfrac{\partial x'_\lambda}{\partial x_\alpha} \cdot A^\alpha$ (see p. 153)

Similarly, for B^α :

(20) $\qquad B'^\lambda = \dfrac{\partial x'_\lambda}{\partial x_\alpha} \cdot B^\alpha$.

Taking corresponding components,

we get, in full:

$$A'^1 = \frac{\partial x_1'}{\partial x_1} \cdot A^1 + \frac{\partial x_1'}{\partial x_2} \cdot A^2$$

and

$$B'^1 = \frac{\partial x_1'}{\partial x_1} \cdot B^1 + \frac{\partial x_1'}{\partial x_2} \cdot B^2.$$

The sum of these gives:

$$A'^1 + B'^1 = \frac{\partial x_1'}{\partial x_1}(A^1 + B^1) + \frac{\partial x_1'}{\partial x_2}(A^2 + B^2).$$

Similarly,

$$A'^2 + B'^2 = \frac{\partial x_2'}{\partial x_1} \cdot (A^1 + B^1) + \frac{\partial x_2'}{\partial x_2} \cdot (A^2 + B^2).$$

Both these results are included in:

$$A'^\lambda + B'^\lambda = \frac{\partial x_\lambda'}{\partial x_\alpha} \cdot (A^\alpha + B^\alpha) \qquad (\lambda, \alpha = 1, 2).$$

Or

(21) $$C'^\lambda = \frac{\partial x_\lambda'}{\partial x_\alpha} \cdot C^\alpha.$$

Thus we see that
the result is
a VECTOR (see p. 155).

Similarly for tensors of
higher ranks.

Furthermore,
note that (21) may be obtained
QUITE MECHANICALLY
by adding (19) and (20)
AS IF each of these were
A SINGLE equation
containing only
A SINGLE term on the right,

161

instead of
A SET OF EQUATIONS
EACH CONTAINING
SEVERAL TERMS ON THE RIGHT.

Thus the notation
AUTOMATICALLY takes care that
the corresponding components
shall be properly added.

This is even more impressive
in the case of multiplication.
Thus,
to multiply

$$(22) \qquad A'^\lambda = \frac{\partial x'_\lambda}{\partial x_\alpha} \cdot A^\alpha$$

by

$$(23) \qquad B'^\mu = \frac{\partial x'_\mu}{\partial x_\beta} \cdot B^\beta, \qquad (\lambda, \mu, \alpha, \beta = 1, 2)$$

we write the result immediately:

$$(24) \quad C'^{\lambda\mu} = \frac{\partial x'_\lambda}{\partial x_\alpha} \cdot \frac{\partial x'_\mu}{\partial x_\beta} \cdot C^{\alpha\beta} \qquad (\lambda, \mu, \alpha, \beta = 1, 2).$$

To convince the reader
that it is quite safe
to write the result so simply,
let us examine (24) carefully
and see whether it really represents
correctly
the result of multiplying (22) by (23).
By "multiplying (22) by (23)"
we mean that
EACH equation of (22) is to be
multiplied by
EACH equation of (23)

163

in the way in which this would be done
in ordinary algebra.
Thus,
we must first multiply

$$A'^1 = \frac{\partial x'_1}{\partial x_1} \cdot A^1 + \frac{\partial x'_1}{\partial x_2} \cdot A^2$$

by

$$B'^1 = \frac{\partial x'_1}{\partial x_1} \cdot B^1 + \frac{\partial x'_1}{\partial x_2} \cdot B^2.$$

We get,

(25) $$A'^1 B'^1 = \frac{\partial x'_1}{\partial x_1} \cdot \frac{\partial x'_1}{\partial x_1} \cdot A^1 B^1 +$$

$$\frac{\partial x'_1}{\partial x_2} \cdot \frac{\partial x'_1}{\partial x_1} \cdot A^2 B^1 +$$

$$\frac{\partial x'_1}{\partial x_1} \cdot \frac{\partial x'_1}{\partial x_2} \cdot A^1 B^2 +$$

$$\frac{\partial x'_1}{\partial x_2} \cdot \frac{\partial x'_1}{\partial x_2} \cdot A^2 B^2.$$

Similarly we shall get
three more such equations,
whose left-hand members are,
respectively,

$$A'^1 B'^2, \ A'^2 B'^1, \ \dot{A}'^2 \cdot B'^2,$$

and whose right-hand members
resemble that of (25).

Now, we may obtain (25) from (24)
by taking $\lambda = 1$, $\mu = 1$,
retaining these values throughout,
since no summation is indicated on λ and μ
[that is, neither λ nor μ is repeated
in any one term of (24)].

164

But since α and β
each OCCUR TWICE
in the term on the right,
they must be allowed to take on
all possible values, namely, 1 and 2 ,
and SUMMED,
thus obtaining (25),
except that we replace $A^\alpha B^\beta$
by the simpler symbol $C^{\alpha\beta}$ *.
Similarly,
by taking $\lambda = 1$, $\mu = 2$ in (24),
and summing on α and β as before,
we obtain another of the equations
mentioned on page 164.

And $\lambda = 2$, $\mu = 1$,
gives the third of these equations;
and finally $\lambda = 2$, $\mu = 2$
gives the fourth and last.

Thus (24) actually does represent
COMPLETELY
the product of (22) and (23)!

Of course, in three-dimensional space,
(22) and (23) would each represent
THREE equations, instead of two,
each containing
THREE terms on the right, instead of two;
and the product of (22) and (23)

*Note that either $A^\alpha B^\beta$ or $C^{\alpha\beta}$
allows for FOUR components:
Namely, A^1B^1 or C^{11},
A^1B^2 or C^{12},
A^2B^1 or C^{21},
and A^2B^2 or C^{22}.
And hence we may use
$C^{\alpha\beta}$ instead of $A^\alpha B^\beta$.

165

would then consist of
NINE equations, instead of four,
each containing
NINE terms on the right, instead of four.
But this result
is still represented by (24)!
And, of course, in four dimensions
(24) would represent
SIXTEEN equations, and so on.

Thus the tensor notation enables us
to multiply
WHOLE SETS OF EQUATIONS
containing MANY TERMS IN EACH,
as EASILY as we multiply
simple monomials in elementary algebra!

Furthermore,
we see from (24)
that
the PRODUCT of two tensors
is also a TENSOR (see page 157),
and, specifically, that
the product of two tensors
each of RANK ONE,
gives a tensor of RANK TWO.

In general,
if two tensors of ranks m and n,
respectively,
are multiplied together,
the result is
a TENSOR OF RANK $m + n$.

This process of multiplying tensors
is called
OUTER multiplication,

166

to distinguish it from
another process known as
INNER multiplication
which is also important
in Tensor Calculus,
and which we shall describe later (page 183).

XVIII. A PHYSICAL ILLUSTRATION.

But first let us discuss
a physical illustration of
ANOTHER KIND OF TENSOR,
A COVARIANT TENSOR:*

Consider an object whose density
is different in different parts of the object.

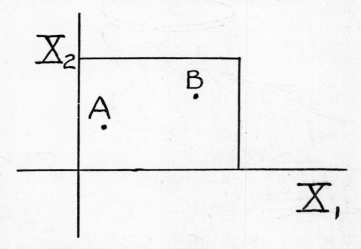

*This is to be distinguished from the
CONTRAVARIANT tensors
discussed on pages 155ff.

167

We may then speak of
the density at a particular point, A.
Now, density is obviously
NOT a directed quantity,
but a SCALAR (see page 127).
And since the density of the given object
is not uniform throughout,
but varies from point to point,
it will vary as we go from A to B.
So that if we designate by ψ
the density at A,
then

$$\frac{\partial \psi}{\partial x_1} \text{ and } \frac{\partial \psi}{\partial x_2}$$

represent, respectively,
the partial variation of ψ
in the x_1 and x_2 directions.
Thus, although ψ itself is NOT
a DIRECTED quantity,
the CHANGE in ψ DOES depend upon
the DIRECTION
and IS therefore a DIRECTED quantity,
whose components are

$$\frac{\partial \psi}{\partial x_1} \text{ and } \frac{\partial \psi}{\partial x^2}.$$

Now let us see
what happens to this quantity when
the coordinate system is changed (see page 149).

We are seeking to express

$$\frac{\partial \psi}{\partial x_1'}, \frac{\partial \psi}{\partial x_2'} \text{ in terms of } \frac{\partial \psi}{\partial x_1}, \frac{\partial \psi}{\partial x_2}.$$

Now if we have three variables,
say, x, y, and z,

169

such that y and z depend upon x,
it is obvious that
the change in z per unit change in x,
IF IT CANNOT BE FOUND DIRECTLY,
may be found by
multiplying
the change in y per unit change in x
by
the change in z per unit change in y,
or,
expressing this in symbols:

$$(26) \qquad \frac{dz}{dx} = \frac{dz}{dy} \cdot \frac{dy}{dx}.$$

In our problem above,
we have the following similar situation:
A change in x_1' will affect
BOTH x_1 and x_2 (see p. 145),
and the resulting changes in x_1 and x_2
will affect ψ;
hence

$$(27) \qquad \frac{\partial \psi}{\partial x_1'} = \frac{\partial \psi}{\partial x_1} \cdot \frac{\partial x_1}{\partial x_1'} + \frac{\partial \psi}{\partial x_2} \cdot \frac{\partial x_2}{\partial x_1'}$$

Note that here we have TWO terms
on the right
instead of only ONE, as in (26),
since the change in x_1'
affects BOTH x_1 and x_2
and these in turn BOTH affect ψ,
whereas in (26),
a change in x affects y,
which in turn affects z,
and that is all there was to it.
Note also that
the curved "∂" is used throughout in (27)
since all the changes here

170

are PARTIAL changes
(see footnote on page 147).
And since ψ is influenced also
by a change in x_2',
this influence may be
similarly represented by

(28)
$$\frac{\partial \psi}{\partial x_2'} = \frac{\partial \psi}{\partial x_1} \cdot \frac{\partial x_1}{\partial x_2'} + \frac{\partial \psi}{\partial x_2} \cdot \frac{\partial x_2}{\partial x_2'}.$$

And, as before,
we may combine (27) and (28)
by means of the abbreviated notation:

(29)
$$\frac{\partial \psi}{\partial x_\mu'} = \frac{\partial \psi}{\partial x_\sigma} \cdot \frac{\partial x_\sigma}{\partial x_\mu'} \qquad (\mu, \sigma = 1, 2)$$

where the occurrence of σ TWICE
in the single term on the right
indicates a summation on σ,
as usual.

And, finally,
writing A_μ' for the two components
represented in $\dfrac{\partial \psi}{\partial x_\mu'}$,

and A_σ for the two components, $\dfrac{\partial \psi}{\partial x_\sigma}$,
we may write (29) as follows:

(30)
$$A_\mu' = \frac{\partial x_\sigma}{\partial x_\mu'} \cdot A_\sigma \qquad (\mu, \sigma = 1, 2).$$

If we now compare (30) with (16)
we note a
VERY IMPORTANT DIFFERENCE,
namely,
that the coefficient on the right in (30)
is the reciprocal of
the coefficient on the right in (16),

171

so that (30) does NOT satisfy
the definition of a vector given in (16).
But it will be remembered that
(16) is the definition of
A CONTRAVARIANT VECTOR ONLY.
And in (30)
we introduce to the reader
the mathematical definition of
A COVARIANT VECTOR.

Note that
to distinguish the two kinds of vectors,
it is customary to write the indices
as SUBscripts in the one case
and as SUPERscripts in the other.*

As before (page 156),
(30) may represent a vector in
any number of dimensions,
depending upon the range of values
given to μ and σ,
and for ANY transformation of coordinates.

Similarly,
A COVARIANT TENSOR OF RANK TWO
is defined by

(31) $$A'_{\alpha\beta} = \frac{\partial x_\gamma}{\partial x'_\alpha} \cdot \frac{\partial x_\delta}{\partial x'_\beta} \cdot A_{\gamma\delta},$$

and so on, for higher ranks.

COMPARE and CONTRAST carefully
(31) and (17).

*Observe that the SUBscripts are used
for the COvariant vectors,
in which the PRIMES in the coefficients
are in the DENOMINATORS (see (30), p. 171).
To remember this more easily
a young student suggests the slogan
"CO, LOW, PRIMES BELOW."

XIX. MIXED TENSORS.

Addition of covariant vectors
is performed in the same simple manner
as for contravariant vectors (see p. 161).
Thus, the SUM of

$$A'_\lambda = \frac{\partial x_\alpha}{\partial x'_\lambda} \cdot A_\alpha$$

and

$$B'_\lambda = \frac{\partial x_\alpha}{\partial x'_\lambda} \cdot B_\alpha$$

is

$$C'_\lambda = \frac{\partial x_\alpha}{\partial x'_\lambda} \cdot C_\alpha .$$

Also,
the operation defined on page 166
as OUTER MULTIPLICATION
is the same for
covariant tensors:
Thus, the OUTER PRODUCT of

$$A'_\lambda = \frac{\partial x_\alpha}{\partial x'_\lambda} \cdot A_\alpha$$

and

$$B'_{\mu\nu} = \frac{\partial x_\beta}{\partial x'_\mu} \cdot \frac{\partial x_\gamma}{\partial x'_\nu} \cdot B_{\beta\gamma}$$

is

$$C'_{\lambda\mu\nu} = \frac{\partial x_\alpha}{\partial x'_\lambda} \cdot \frac{\partial x_\beta}{\partial x'_\mu} \cdot \frac{\partial x_\gamma}{\partial x'_\nu} \cdot C_{\alpha\beta\gamma}$$

Furthermore,
it is also possible to multiply
a COVARIANT tensor by
a CONTRAVARIANT one,
thus,

the OUTER PRODUCT of

$$A'_\lambda = \frac{\partial x_\alpha}{\partial x'_\lambda} \cdot A_\alpha$$

and

$$B'^\mu = \frac{\partial x'_\mu}{\partial x_\beta} \cdot B^\beta$$

is

(32) $$C'^\mu_\lambda = \frac{\partial x_\alpha}{\partial x'_\lambda} \cdot \frac{\partial x'_\mu}{\partial x_\beta} \cdot C^\beta_\alpha.$$

Comparison of (32) with (31) and (17)
shows that it is
NEITHER a covariant
NOR a contravariant tensor.
It is called
A MIXED TENSOR of rank TWO.

More generally,
the OUTER PRODUCT of

(33) $$A'^{\alpha\beta}_\gamma = \frac{\partial x_\nu}{\partial x'_\gamma} \cdot \frac{\partial x'_\alpha}{\partial x_\lambda} \cdot \frac{\partial x'_\beta}{\partial x_\mu} \cdot A^{\lambda\mu}_\nu.$$

and

(34) $$B'^\kappa_\delta = \frac{\partial x_\sigma}{\partial x'_\delta} \cdot \frac{\partial x'_\kappa}{\partial x_\rho} \cdot B^\rho_\sigma.$$

is

(35) $$C'^{\alpha\beta\kappa}_{\gamma\delta} = \frac{\partial x_\nu}{\partial x'_\gamma} \cdot \frac{\partial x_\sigma}{\partial x'_\delta} \cdot \frac{\partial x'_\alpha}{\partial x_\lambda} \cdot \frac{\partial x'_\beta}{\partial x_\mu} \cdot \frac{\partial x'_\kappa}{\partial x_\rho} \cdot C^{\lambda\mu\rho}_{\nu\sigma}.$$

That is,
if any two tensors of ranks m and n,
respectively,
are multiplied together
so as to form their
OUTER PRODUCT,
the result is a TENSOR of rank m + n;

175

thus, the rank of (33) is 3 ,
and that of (34) is 2 ,
hence,
the rank of their outer product, (35),
is 5.

Furthermore,
suppose the tensor of rank m
is a MIXED tensor,
having m_1 indices of covariance*
and m_2 indices of contravariance†
(such that $m_1 + m_2 = m$),
and suppose the tensor of rank n
has n_1 indices of covariance*
and n_2 indices of contravariance,†
then,
their outer product will be
a MIXED tensor having
$m_1 + n_1$ indices of covariance*
and
$m_2 + n_2$ indices of contravariance.†

All this has already been illustrated
in the special case given above:
Thus,
(33) has ONE index of covariance (γ)
and (34) also has
ONE index of covariance (δ),
therefore their outer product, (35),
has TWO indices of covariance (γ , δ);
and similarly,
since (33) has
TWO indices of contravariance (α, β)
and (34) has

* SUBscripts.
† SUPERscripts.

176

ONE index of contravariance (κ),
their outer product, (35),
has
THREE indices of contravariance (α, β, κ).

We hope the reader appreciates
the fact that
although it takes many words
to describe these processes
it is extremely EASY
to DO them
with the AID of the
TENSOR NOTATION.
Thus the outer product of

$$A^{\alpha\beta} \text{ and } B_{\gamma\delta}$$

is simply $C^{\alpha\beta}_{\gamma\delta}$!

Let us remind him, however, that
behind this notation,
the processes are really complicated:
Thus (33) represents
a whole SET of equations*
each having MANY* terms on the right.
And (34) also represents
a SET of equations†
each having MANY† terms on the right.
And their outer product, (35),
is obtained by
multiplying

*Namely, EIGHT for two-dimensional space,
 TWENTY-SEVEN for three-dimensional,
 SIXTY-FOUR for four-dimensional,
 and so on.
†Four for two-dimensional space,
 NINE for three-dimensional space,
 SIXTEEN for four-dimensional space,
 and so on.

177

EACH equation of (33) by
EACH one of (34),
resulting in a SET of equations, (35),
containing
THIRTY-TWO equations for
two-dimensional space,
TWO HUNDRED AND FORTY-THREE for
three-dimensional space,
ONE THOUSAND AND TWENTY-FOUR for
four-dimensional space,
and so on.
And all with a
correspondingly large number of terms
on the right of each equation!

And yet
"any child can operate it"
as easily as
pushing a button.

XX. CONTRACTION AND DIFFERENTIATION.

This powerful and
easily operated machine,
the TENSOR CALCULUS,
was devised and perfected by
the mathematicians
Ricci and Levi-Civita
in about 1900,
and was known to very few people
until Einstein made use of it.
Since then it has become
widely known,
and we hope that this little book
will make it intelligible
even to laymen.

178

But what use did Einstein make of it?
What is its connection with Relativity?

We are nearly ready to fulfill
the promise made on page 125.

When we have explained
two more operations with tensors,
namely,
CONTRACTION and DIFFERENTIATION,
we shall be able to derive
the promised CURVATURE TENSOR,
from which
Einstein's Law of Gravitation
is obtained.

Consider the mixed tensor (33), p. 175:
suppose we replace in it

$$\gamma \text{ by } \alpha,$$

obtaining

$$(36) \qquad A'^{\alpha\beta}_{\alpha} = \frac{\partial x_\nu}{\partial x'_\alpha} \cdot \frac{\partial x'_\alpha}{\partial x_\lambda} \cdot \frac{\partial x'_\beta}{\partial x_\mu} \cdot A^{\lambda\mu}_\nu.$$

By the summation convention (p. 152),
the left-hand member is to be summed on α,
so that (36) now represents
only TWO equations instead of eight,*
each of which contains
TWO terms on the left instead of one;
furthermore,
on the RIGHT,
since α occurs twice here,
we must sum on α
for each pair of values of ν and λ:
Now,

*See p. 177.

when ν happens to have a value
DIFFERENT from λ,

then

$$\frac{\partial x_\nu}{\partial x'_\alpha} \cdot \frac{\partial x'_\alpha}{\partial x_\lambda} = \frac{\partial x_\nu}{\partial x_\lambda} = 0$$

BECAUSE
the x's are NOT functions of each other
(but only of the x''s)
and therefore
there is NO variation of x_ν
with respect to
a DIFFERENT x, namely x_λ.
Thus coefficients of $A_\nu^{\lambda\mu}$ when $\lambda \neq \nu$
will all be ZERO
and will make these terms drop out.
BUT
When $\lambda = \nu$,
then

$$\frac{\partial x_\nu}{\partial x'_\alpha} \cdot \frac{\partial x'_\alpha}{\partial x_\lambda} = \frac{\partial x_\lambda}{\partial x'_\alpha} \cdot \frac{\partial x'_\alpha}{\partial x_\lambda} = 1.$$

Thus (36) becomes

(37) $\qquad A'^{\alpha\beta}_\alpha = \dfrac{\partial x'_\beta}{\partial x_\mu} \cdot A_\lambda^{\lambda\mu}$

in which we must still
sum on the right
for λ and μ.

To make all this clearer,
let us write out explicitly
the two equations represented by (37):

$$\begin{cases} A'^{11}_1 + A'^{21}_2 = \dfrac{\partial x'_1}{\partial x_1}\,(A_1^{11} + A_2^{21}) + \dfrac{\partial x'_1}{\partial x_2}\,(A_1^{12} + A_2^{22}) \\[2ex] A'^{12}_1 + A'^{22}_2 = \dfrac{\partial x'_2}{\partial x_1}\,(A_1^{11} + A_2^{21}) + \dfrac{\partial x'_2}{\partial x_2}\,(A_1^{12} + A_2^{22}). \end{cases}$$

181

Thus (37) may be written more briefly:

(38)
$$C'^{\beta} = \frac{\partial x'_{\beta}}{\partial x_{\mu}} \cdot C^{\mu}$$

where

$$C'^1 = A'^{11}_1 + A'^{21}_2,$$
$$C'^2 = A'^{12}_1 + A'^{22}_2$$

and

$$C^1 = A^{11}_1 + A^{21}_2,$$
$$C^2 = A^{12}_1 + A^{22}_2.$$

In other words,
by making one upper and one lower index
ALIKE
in (33),
we have REDUCED
a tensor of rank THREE to
a tensor of rank ONE.

The important thing to note is
that this process of reduction
or CONTRACTION,
as it is called,
leads again to
A TENSOR,
and it is obvious that
for every such contraction
the rank is reduced by TWO,
since for every such contraction
two of the partial derivatives in
the coefficient
cancel out (see page 181).

We shall see later
how important this process of contraction is.

Now,
if we form the OUTER PRODUCT of two tensors,
in the way already described (p. 175)

182

and if the result is
a mixed tensor,
then,
by contracting this mixed tensor
as shown above,
we get a tensor which is called
an INNER PRODUCT
in contrast to
their OUTER PRODUCT.

Thus the OUTER product of

$$A_{\alpha\beta} \text{ and } B^\gamma$$

is $\qquad C^\gamma_{\alpha\beta}$ (see page 177);
now, if in this result
we replace γ by β,
obtaining

$$C^\beta_{\alpha\beta} \text{ or } D_\alpha \text{ (see pages 180 to 182),}$$

then $\qquad D_\alpha$ is an INNER product of
$$A_{\alpha\beta} \text{ and } B^\gamma.$$

And now we come to
DIFFERENTIATION.

We must remind the reader that
if

$$y = uv$$

where y, u, and v are variables,
then

$$\frac{dy}{dx} = u\frac{dv}{dx} + v\frac{du^*}{dx}.$$

Applying this principle to
the differentiation of

$$(39) \qquad A'^\mu = \frac{\partial x'_\mu}{\partial x_\sigma} \cdot A^\sigma,$$

*See any book on differential calculus.

183

with respect to x'_ν,
we get:

(40)
$$\frac{\partial A'^\mu}{\partial x'_\nu} = \frac{\partial x'_\mu}{\partial x_\sigma} \cdot \frac{\partial A^\sigma}{\partial x'_\nu} + A^\sigma \cdot \frac{\partial^2 x'_\mu}{\partial x_\sigma \cdot \partial x'_\nu} .$$

Or, since

$$\frac{\partial A^\sigma}{\partial x'_\nu} = \frac{\partial A^\sigma}{\partial x_\tau} \cdot \frac{\partial x_\tau}{\partial x'_\nu} , \text{ by (26),}$$

hence (40) becomes

(41)
$$\frac{\partial A'^\mu}{\partial x_\nu} = \frac{\partial x'_\mu}{\partial x_\sigma} \cdot \frac{\partial x_\tau}{\partial x'_\nu} \cdot \frac{\partial A^\sigma}{\partial x_\tau} + \frac{\partial^2 x'_\mu}{\partial x_\sigma \cdot \partial x'_\nu} \cdot A^\sigma .$$

From (41) we see that
if the second term on the right
were not present,
then (41) would represent
a mixed tensor of rank two.
And, in certain special cases,
this second term does vanish,
so that
in SUCH cases,
differentiation of a tensor
leads to another tensor
whose rank is one more than
the rank of the given tensor.
Such a special case is the one
in which the coefficients

$$\frac{\partial x'_\mu}{\partial x_\sigma}$$

in (39)
are constants,
as in (13) on page 147,
since the coefficients in (13)
are the same as those in (11) or (10);

184

and are therefore functions of θ,
θ being the angle through which
the axes were rotated (page 141),
and therefore a constant.
In other words,
when the transformation of coordinates
is of the simple type
described on page 141 ,
then
ordinary differentiation of a tensor
leads to a tensor.

BUT, IN GENERAL,
these coefficients are NOT constants,
and so,
IN GENERAL
differentiation of a tensor
does NOT give a tensor
as is evident from (41).

BUT
there is a process called
COVARIANT DIFFERENTIATION
which ALWAYS leads to a tensor,
and which we shall presently describe.

We cannot emphasize too often
the IMPORTANCE
of any process which
leads to a tensor,
since tensors represent
the "FACTS" of our universe
(see page 149).

And, besides,
we shall have to employ
COVARIANT DIFFERENTIATION
in deriving

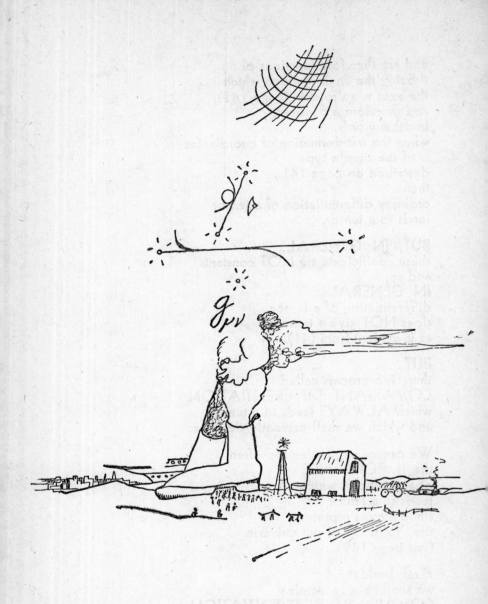

the long-promised
CURVATURE TENSOR
and
EINSTEIN'S LAW OF GRAVITATION.

XXI. THE LITTLE g's.

To explain covariant differentiation
we must first refer the reader back
to chapter XIII,
in which it was shown that
the distance between two points,
or, rather, the square of this distance,
namely, ds^2,
takes on various forms
depending upon
(a) the surface in question
and
(b) the coordinate system used.

But now,
with the aid of the remarkable notation
which we have since explained,
we can include
ALL these expressions for ds^2
in the SINGLE expression

(42) $$ds^2 = g_{\mu\nu} \cdot dx_\mu \cdot dx_\nu \, ;$$

and, indeed,
this holds NOT ONLY for
ANY SURFACE,
but also for
any THREE-dimensional space,
or FOUR-dimensional,

or, in general,
any n-dimensional space!*

Thus, to show how (42) represents
equation (3) on page 116 ,
we take $\mu = 1 , 2$ and $\nu = 1 , 2$,
obtaining

(43) $ds^2 = g_{11}dx_1 \cdot dx_1 + g_{12}dx_1 \cdot dx_2 +$
$g_{21}dx_2 \cdot dx_1 + g_{22}dx_2 \cdot dx_2 ,$

since the presence of μ and ν
TWICE
in the term on the right in (42)
requires SUMMATION on both μ and ν.†
Of course (43) may be written:

(44) $ds^2 = g_{11}dx_1^2 + g_{12}dx_1dx_2 +$
$g_{21}dx_2dx_1 + g_{22}dx_2^2 ;$ ‡

and, comparing (44) with (3),
we find that
the coefficients in (3)
have the particular values:

$$g_{11} = 1 , g_{12} = 0 , g_{21} = 0 , g_{22} = 1.$$

*Except only at a so-called "singular point"
of a space;
that is,
a point at which
matter is actually located.
In other words,
(42) holds for any region AROUND matter.
†See page 152.
‡Note that in dx_1^2 (as well as in dx_2^2)
the upper "2" is really an exponent
and NOT a SUPERSCRIPT
since (44) is an
ordinary algebraic equation
and is NOT in the
ABBREVIATED TENSOR NOTATION.

Similarly, in (6) on page 120,

$$g_{11} = r^2, \; g_{12} = 0, \; g_{21} = 0, \; g_{22} = R^2;$$

and, in (7) on page 123,

$$g_{11} = 1, \; g_{12} = -\cos\alpha, \; g_{21} = -\cos\alpha, \; g_{22} = 1,$$

and so on.

Note that g_{12} and g_{21} have
the SAME value.
And indeed, in general

$$g_{\mu\nu} = g_{\nu\mu}$$

in (42) on page 187.

Of course, if, in (42),
we take $\mu = 1, 2, 3$ and $\nu = 1, 2, 3,$
we shall get the value for ds^2
in a THREE-dimensional space:

(45) $\quad ds^2 = g_{11}dx_1^2 + g_{12}dx_1 \cdot dx_2 + g_{13}dx_1 \cdot dx_3$
$\qquad\qquad\quad + g_{21}dx_2 \cdot dx_1 + g_{22}dx_2^2 + g_{23}dx_2 \cdot dx_3$
$\qquad\qquad\quad + g_{31}dx_3 \cdot dx_1 + g_{32}dx_3 \cdot dx_2 + g_{33}dx_3^2.$

Thus, in particular,
for ordinary Euclidean three-space,
using the common rectangular coordinates,
we now have:

$$g_{11} = 1, \; g_{22} = 1, \; g_{33} = 1,$$

and all the other g's are zero,
so that (42) becomes,
for THIS PARTICULAR CASE,
the familiar expression

$$ds^2 = dx_1^2 + dx_2^2 + dx_3^2$$

or

$$ds^2 = dx^2 + dy^2 + dz^2;$$

and similarly for
higher dimensions.

Thus, for a given space,
two-, three-, four-, or n-dimensional,
and for a given set of coordinates,
we get a certain set of g's.

It is easy to show* that
any such set of g's,
(which is represented by $g_{\mu\nu}$)
constitutes
the COMPONENTS of a TENSOR,
and, in fact, that
it is a
COVARIANT TENSOR OF RANK TWO,
and hence is appropriately
designated with TWO SUBscripts†:

$$g_{\mu\nu} \ .$$

Let us now briefly sum up
the story so far:

By introducing
the Principle of Equivalence
Einstein replaced the idea of
a "force of gravity"
by the concept of
a geometrical space (Chap. XII).
And since a space
is characterized by its g's,
the knowledge of the g's of a space
is essential to a study of
how things move in the space,
and hence essential
to an understanding of
Einstein's Law of Gravitation.

*See p. 313.
†See p. 172.

XXII. OUR LAST DETOUR.

As we said before (page 185),
to derive the
Einstein Law of Gravitation,
we must employ
COVARIANT DIFFERENTIATION.
Now, the COVARIANT DERIVATIVE of a tensor
contains certain quantities known as
CHRISTOFFEL SYMBOLS *
which are functions of the tensor $g_{\mu\nu}$
discussed in chapter XXI,
and also of another set $g^{\mu\nu}$
(note the SUPERscripts here)
which we shall now describe:

For simplicity,
let us limit ourselves for the moment
to TWO-dimensional space,
that is,
let us take $\mu = 1, 2$ and $\nu = 1, 2$;
then $g_{\mu\nu}$ will have
FOUR components,
namely,
the four coefficients on the right
in (44).
And let us arrange these coefficients
in a SQUARE ARRAY, thus:

$$\left\| \begin{array}{cc} g_{11} & g_{12} \\ g_{21} & g_{22} \end{array} \right\|$$

which is called a MATRIX.
Now since $g_{12} = g_{21}$ (see page 189)

*Named for the mathematician, Christoffel.

this is called a
SYMMETRIC MATRIX,
since it is symmetric with respect to
the principal diagonal
(that is, the one which starts
in the upper left-hand corner).

If we now replace the double bars
on each side of the matrix
by SINGLE bars,
as shown in the following:

$$\begin{vmatrix} g_{11} & g_{12} \\ g_{21} & g_{22} \end{vmatrix}$$

we get what is known as
a DETERMINANT.*
The reader must carefully
DISTINGUISH between

*The reader probably knows that
a square array of numbers
with single bars on each side

$$\begin{vmatrix} 5 & 6 \\ 2 & 3 \end{vmatrix}$$

is called a determinant,
and that its value is found thus:

$$5 \times 3 - 6 \times 2 = 15 - 12 = 3.$$

Or, more generally,

$$\begin{vmatrix} a & b \\ c & d \end{vmatrix} = ad - bc.$$

A determinant does not necessarily
have to have TWO rows and columns,
but may have n rows and n columns,
and is then said to be of order n.
The way to find the VALUE of
a determinant of the nth order
is described in any book on
college algebra.

193

a square array with SINGLE bars
from one with DOUBLE bars:
The FORMER is a DETERMINANT
and has a SINGLE VALUE
found by combining the "elements"
in a certain way
as mentioned in the foot-note on p. 193.
Whereas,
the DOUBLE-barred array
is a set of SEPARATE "elements,"
NOT to be COMBINED in any way.
They may be just
the coefficients of the separate terms
on the right in (44),
which,
as we mentioned on page 190,
are the separate COMPONENTS of a tensor.

The determinant on page 193
may be designated more briefly by

$$| g_{\mu\nu} |, \qquad (\mu = 1, 2; \ \nu = 1, 2)$$

or, still better, simply by g.

And now let us form a new square array
in the following manner:
DIVIDE the COFACTOR* of EACH ELEMENT
of the determinant on page 193
by the value of the whole determinant,
namely, by g,
thus obtaining the corresponding element of
the NEW array.

*For readers unfamiliar with determinants
  this term is explained on p. 195.

194

The COFACTOR of a given element
of a determinant
is found by striking out
the row and column containing the given element,
and evaluating the
determinant which is left over,
prefixing the sign + or −
according to a certain rule:
Thus, in the determinant

$$\begin{vmatrix} 5 & 2 & 3 \\ 4 & 1 & 0 \\ 6 & 8 & 7 \end{vmatrix}$$

the cofactor of the element 5, is:

$$+ \begin{vmatrix} 1 & 0 \\ 8 & 7 \end{vmatrix} = 1 \times 7 - 8 \times 0 = 7 - 0 = 7.$$

Similarly, the cofactor of 4 is:

$$- \begin{vmatrix} 2 & 3 \\ 8 & 7 \end{vmatrix} = - (14 - 24) = 10;$$

and so on.
Note that in the first case
we prefixed the sign + ,
while in the second case
we prefixed a − .
The rule is:
prefix a + or − according as
the NUMBER of steps required to go
from the first element
(that is, the one in
the upper left-hand corner)
to the given element,
is EVEN or ODD, respectively;
thus to go from "5" to "4"
it takes one step,
hence the cofactor of "4" must have
a MINUS prefixed before

$$\begin{vmatrix} 2 & 3 \\ 8 & 7 \end{vmatrix}.$$

But all this is more thoroughly
explained in any book on
college algebra.

Let us now go back
to the array described
at the bottom of p. 194.

This new array,
which we shall designate by $g^{\mu\nu}$
can also be shown to be
a TENSOR,
and, this time,
A CONTRAVARIANT TENSOR
OF RANK TWO.
That it is also SYMMETRIC
can easily be shown by the reader.

We can now give the definition
of the Christoffel symbol
which we need.
It is designated by $\{\mu\nu, \lambda\}$

and is a symbol for:

(46) $\qquad \dfrac{1}{2}\, g^{\lambda\alpha} \left(\dfrac{\partial g_{\mu\alpha}}{\partial x_\nu} + \dfrac{\partial g_{\nu\alpha}}{\partial x_\mu} - \dfrac{\partial g_{\mu\nu}}{\partial x_\alpha} \right)$.

In other words,
the above-mentioned Christoffel symbol*
involves partial derivatives of
the coefficients in (44),
combined as shown in (46)
and multiplied by
the components of the tensor $g^{\mu\nu}$.
Thus, in two-dimensional space,

*There are other Christoffel symbols,
  but we promised the reader
  to introduce only the
  barest minimum of mathematics
  necessary for our purpose!

196

since μ, ν, λ, α each have the values 1, 2,
we have, for example,

$$\{11, 1\} = \frac{1}{2} \, g^{11} \left(\frac{\partial g_{11}}{\partial x_1} + \frac{\partial g_{11}}{\partial x_1} - \frac{\partial g_{11}}{\partial x_1}\right)$$

$$+ \frac{1}{2} \, g^{12} \left(\frac{\partial g_{12}}{\partial x_1} + \frac{\partial g_{12}}{\partial x_1} - \frac{\partial g_{11}}{\partial x_2}\right),$$

and similarly for the remaining
SEVEN values of

$$\{\mu\nu, \lambda\}$$

obtained by allowing μ, ν and λ
to take on their two values for each.

Note that in evaluating $\{11, 1\}$ above,
we SUMMED on the α,
allowing α to take on BOTH values, 1, 2,
BECAUSE
if (46) were multiplied out,
EACH TERM would contain α TWICE,
and this calls for
SUMMATION on the α (see page 152).
Now that we know the meaning of
the 3-index Christoffel symbol

$$\{\mu\nu, \lambda\},$$

we are ready to define
the covariant derivative of a tensor,
from which it is only a step to
the new Law of Gravitation.

If A_σ is a covariant tensor of rank one,
its COVARIANT DERIVATIVE
with respect to x_τ
is DEFINED as:

(47) $\qquad \dfrac{\partial A_\sigma}{\partial x_\tau} - \{\sigma\tau, \alpha\} \, A_\alpha.$

197

It can be shown to be a TENSOR —
in fact, it is a
COVARIANT TENSOR OF RANK TWO*
and may therefore be designated by

$$A_{\sigma\tau} .$$

Similarly,
if we have
a contravariant tensor of rank one,
represented by A^σ ,
its COVARIANT DERIVATIVE
with respect to x_τ
is the TENSOR:

(48)
$$A_\tau^\sigma = \frac{\partial A^\sigma}{\partial x_\tau} + \{\sigma\epsilon,\tau\} A^\epsilon .$$

Or,
starting with tensors of rank TWO,
we have the following three cases:

(a) starting with the
CONTRAVARIANT tensor, $A^{\sigma\tau}$,
we get the COVARIANT DERIVATIVE:

$$A_\rho^{\sigma\tau} = \frac{\partial A^{\sigma\tau}}{\partial x_\rho} + \{\rho\epsilon,\sigma\} A^{\epsilon\tau} + \{\rho\epsilon,\tau\} A^{\tau\epsilon} ,$$

(b) from the MIXED tensor, A_σ^τ ,
we get the COVARIANT DERIVATIVE:

$$A_{\sigma\rho}^\tau = \frac{\partial A_\sigma^\tau}{\partial x_\rho} - \{\rho\sigma,\epsilon\} A_\epsilon^\tau + \{\rho\epsilon,\tau\} A_\sigma^\epsilon ,$$

*See p. 60 of
"The Mathematical Theory of Relativity," by
A. S. Eddington,
the 1930 Edition.

198

(c) from the COVARIANT tensor, $A_{\sigma\tau}$,
we get the COVARIANT DERIVATIVE:

$$A_{\sigma\tau\rho} = \frac{\partial A_{\sigma\tau}}{\partial x_\rho} - \{\sigma\rho, \epsilon\} \, A_{\epsilon\tau} - \{\tau\rho, \epsilon\} \, A_{\sigma\epsilon}.$$

And similarly for the
COVARIANT DERIVATIVES
of tensors of higher ranks.

Note that IN ALL CASES
COVARIANT DIFFERENTIATION
OF A TENSOR
leads to a TENSOR having
ONE MORE UNIT OF
COVARIANT CHARACTER
than the given tensor.

Of course since
the covariant derivative of a tensor
is itself a tensor,
we may find
ITS covariant derivative
which is then the
SECOND COVARIANT DERIVATIVE of
the original tensor,
and so on for
higher covariant derivatives.

Note also that
when the g's happen to be constants,
as, for example,
in the case of a Euclidean plane,
using rectangular coordinates,
in which case we have (see p. 188)

$$ds_2 = dx_1^2 + dx_2^2,$$

so that

$$g_{11} = 1 \, , \, g_{12} = 0 \, , \, g_{21} = 0 \, , \, g_{22} = 1 \, ,$$

199

all constants,
then obviously
the Christoffel symbols here
are all ZERO,
since the derivative of a constant is zero,
and every term of the
Christoffel symbol
has such a derivative as a factor,*

so that (47) becomes simply $\dfrac{\partial A_\sigma}{\partial x_\tau}$.

That is, in this case,
the covariant derivative becomes
simply the ordinary derivative.
But of course
this is NOT so IN GENERAL.

XXIII. THE CURVATURE TENSOR AT LAST.

Having now built up the necessary machinery,
the reader will have no trouble
in following the derivation of
the new Law of Gravitation.

Starting with the tensor, A_σ ,
form its covariant derivative
with respect to x_τ :

$$(49) \qquad A_{\sigma\tau} = \frac{\partial A_\sigma}{\partial x_\tau} - \{\sigma\tau, \alpha\}\, A_\alpha. \text{(see p. 197).}$$

*See page 196.

Now form the covariant derivative
of $A_{\sigma\tau}$ (see page 199)
with respect to x_ρ :

(50) $\qquad A_{\sigma\tau\rho} = \dfrac{\partial A_{\sigma\tau}}{\partial x_\rho} - \{\sigma\rho, \epsilon\} A_{\epsilon\tau} - \{\tau\rho, \epsilon\} A_{\sigma\epsilon}$

obtaining
a SECOND covariant derivative of A_σ ,
which is a
COVARIANT TENSOR
OF RANK THREE.
Substituting (49) in (50),
we get

$$A_{\sigma\tau\rho} = \frac{\partial^2 A_\sigma}{\partial x_\tau \partial x_\rho} - \{\sigma\tau, \alpha\} \frac{\partial A_\alpha}{\partial x_\rho} - A_\alpha \frac{\partial}{\partial x_\rho} \{\sigma\tau, \alpha\}$$

$$- \{\sigma\rho, \epsilon\} \left[\frac{\partial A_\epsilon}{\partial x_\tau} - \{\epsilon\tau, \alpha\} A_\alpha \right]$$

$$- \{\tau\rho, \epsilon\} \left[\frac{\partial A_\sigma}{\partial x_\epsilon} - \{\sigma\epsilon, \alpha\} A_\alpha \right]$$

or

(51) $A_{\sigma\tau\rho} = \dfrac{\partial^2 A_\sigma}{\partial x_\tau \partial x_\rho} - \{\sigma\tau, \alpha\} \dfrac{\partial A_\alpha}{\partial x_\rho}$

$$- A_\alpha \frac{\partial}{\partial x_\rho} \{\sigma\tau, \alpha\} - \{\sigma\rho, \epsilon\} \frac{\partial A_\epsilon}{\partial x_\tau}$$

$$+ \{\sigma\rho, \epsilon\} \{\epsilon\tau, \alpha\} A_\alpha - \{\tau\rho, \epsilon\} \frac{\partial A_\sigma}{\partial x_\epsilon}$$

$$+ \{\tau\rho, \epsilon\} \{\sigma\epsilon, \alpha\} A_\alpha .$$

202

If we had taken these derivatives
in the REVERSE order,
namely,
FIRST with respect to x_ρ
and THEN with respect to x_τ,
we would of course have obtained
the following result instead:

$$(52) \quad A_{\sigma\rho\tau} = \frac{\partial^2 A_\sigma}{\partial x_\rho \partial x_\tau} - \{\sigma\rho\,,\,\alpha\}\frac{\partial A_\alpha}{\partial x_\tau}$$

$$- A_\alpha \frac{\partial}{\partial x_\tau}\{\sigma\rho\,,\,\alpha\} - \{\sigma\tau\,,\,\epsilon\}\frac{\partial A_\epsilon}{\partial x_\rho}$$

$$+ \{\sigma\tau\,,\,\epsilon\}\{\epsilon\rho\,,\,\alpha\}\,A_\alpha$$

$$- \{\rho\tau\,,\,\epsilon\}\frac{\partial A_\sigma}{\partial x_\epsilon} + \{\rho\tau\,,\,\epsilon\}\{\sigma\epsilon\,,\,\alpha\}\,A_\alpha$$

which is again
a COVARIANT TENSOR OF RANK THREE.

Now,
comparing (51) with (52)
we shall find that they are
NOT alike THROUGHOUT:
Only SOME of the terms are the
SAME in both,
but the remaining terms are different.

Let us see:

the FIRST term in each is:

$\dfrac{\partial^2 A_\sigma}{\partial x_\tau \partial x_\rho}$ and $\dfrac{\partial^2 A_\sigma}{\partial x_\rho \partial x_\tau}$, respectively.

These, by ordinary calculus,

203

ARE the same.*
The SECOND term of (51)
is the same as
the FOURTH term of (52)
since the occurrence of α (or ϵ)
TWICE in the same term
implies a SUMMATION
and it is therefore immaterial
what letter is used (α or ϵ) ! †
Similarly for
the FOURTH term of (51)
and the SECOND of (52).
The SIXTH term (and the SEVENTH)
is the same in both
since the reversal of τ and ρ in

$$\{\tau\rho , \epsilon\}$$

*For, suppose that z is a function of x and y ,

as, for example, $z = x^2 + 2xy$.

Then $\dfrac{\partial z}{\partial x} = 2x + 2y$ (treating y as constant)

and $\dfrac{\partial^2 z}{\partial x \cdot \partial y} = 2$ (treating x as constant).

And, if we reverse the order of differentiation,
finding FIRST the derivative with respect to y
and THEN with respect to x ,
we would get

$$\frac{\partial z}{\partial y} = 2y \text{ (treating x as constant)}$$

and $\dfrac{\partial^2 z}{\partial y \cdot \partial x} = 2$ (treating y as constant)

the SAME FINAL result.
And this is true IN GENERAL.

† An index which is thus easily replaceable is called a "dummy"!

does not alter the value of
this Christoffel symbol:
This can easily be seen by referring
to the definition of this symbol,*
and remembering that the tensor $g_{\mu\nu}$
is SYMMETRIC,

that is, $g_{\mu\nu} = g_{\nu\mu}$ (see page 189).

Similarly the last term is the same
in both (51) and (52).

But the THIRD and FIFTH terms of (51)
are NOT equal to any of the terms in (52).
Hence by subtraction we get

$$A_{\sigma\tau\rho} - A_{\sigma\rho\tau} = \{\sigma\rho, \epsilon\} \{\epsilon\tau, \alpha\} A_\alpha - A_\alpha \frac{\partial}{\partial x_\rho} \{\sigma\tau, \alpha\}$$

$$+ A_\alpha \frac{\partial}{\partial x_\tau} \{\sigma\rho, \alpha\} - \{\sigma\tau, \epsilon\} \{\epsilon\rho, \alpha\} A_\alpha$$

or

$$(53) \quad A_{\sigma\tau\rho} - A_{\sigma\rho\tau} = \left[\{\sigma\rho, \epsilon\} \{\epsilon\tau, \alpha\} - \frac{\partial}{\partial x_\rho} \{\sigma\tau, \alpha\} \right.$$

$$\left. + \frac{\partial}{\partial x_\tau} \{\sigma\rho, \alpha\} - \{\sigma\tau, \epsilon\} \{\epsilon\rho, \alpha\} \right] A_\alpha.$$

And since addition (or subtraction)
of tensors
gives a result which is itself a tensor (see page 161)
the left-hand member of (53) is
A COVARIANT TENSOR OF RANK THREE,
hence of course the right-hand member
is also such a tensor.
But, now,
since A_α is an arbitrary covariant vector,

*See page 196.

its coefficient,
namely, the quantity in square brackets,
must also be a tensor
according to the theorem on p. 312.
Furthermore,
this bracketed expression
must be a MIXED tensor of RANK FOUR,
since on inner multiplication by A_a
it must give a result which is
of rank THREE;
and indeed it must be of the form

$$B^\alpha_{\sigma\tau\rho}$$

(see page 313).
This
AT LAST
is the long-promised
CURVATURE TENSOR (page 187),
and is known as
THE RIEMANN-CHRISTOFFEL TENSOR.

Let us examine it carefully
so that we may appreciate
its meaning and value.

XXIV. OF WHAT USE IS THE CURVATURE TENSOR?

In the first place
we must remember that
it is an abbreviated notation for
the expression in square brackets
in (53) on page 205;
in which,
if we substitute for the Christoffel symbols,

$\{\sigma\rho, \epsilon\}$ and so on,
their values in accordance with
the definition on page 196,
we find that we have
an expression containing
first and second partial derivatives
of the g's,
which are themselves the coefficients
in the expression for ds^2 (see p. 187).

How many components does
the Riemann-Christoffel tensor have?
Obviously that depends upon the
dimensionality of the space
under consideration.
Thus, if we are studying
a two-dimensional surface,
then each of the indices,
will have two possible values,
so that $B^{\alpha}_{\sigma\tau\rho}$ would then have
sixteen components.
Similarly,
in three-dimensional space
it would have 3^4 or 81 components,
and so on.
For the purposes of Relativity,
in which we have to deal with
a FOUR-dimensional continuum
this tensor has 4^4 or 256 components!

We hasten to add that
it is not quite so bad as that,
as we can easily see:
In the first place,
if, in this tensor,*

*That is, in the expression in square brackets
in (53) on page 205.

207

we interchange τ and ρ,
the result is merely to change its sign.‡
Hence,
of the possible 16 combinations of τ and ρ,
only 6 are independent:
This is in itself so interesting
that we shall linger here for a moment:
Suppose we have 16 quantities, $a_{\alpha\beta}$,
(where $\alpha = 1, 2, 3, 4$, and $\beta = 1, 2, 3, 4$),
which we may arrange as follows:

$$\begin{Vmatrix} a_{11} & a_{12} & a_{13} & a_{14} \\ a_{21} & a_{22} & a_{23} & a_{24} \\ a_{31} & a_{32} & a_{33} & a_{34} \\ a_{41} & a_{42} & a_{43} & a_{44} \end{Vmatrix}$$

And suppose that $a_{\alpha\beta} = -a_{\beta\alpha}$
(that is, a reversal of the two subscripts
results only in a change of sign of the term),
then, since $a_{11} = -a_{11}$ implies that $a_{11} = 0$,
and similarly for the remaining terms
in the principal diagonal,
hence,
the above array becomes:

$$\begin{Vmatrix} 0 & a_{12} & a_{13} & a_{14} \\ -a_{12} & 0 & a_{23} & a_{24} \\ -a_{13} & -a_{23} & 0 & a_{34} \\ -a_{14} & -a_{24} & -a_{34} & 0 \end{Vmatrix}$$

Thus there are only
SIX distinct quantities
instead of sixteen.
Such an array is called
ANTISYMMETRIC.

‡The reader would do well to compare this expression
with the one obtained from it by an interchange of τ and
ρ throughout.

Compare this with the definition of
a SYMMETRIC array on page 193.‡
And so,
to come back to the discussion on page 208,
we now have
six combinations of τ and ρ
to be used with
sixteen combinations of σ and α,
giving 6×16 or 96 components
instead of 256.

Furthermore,
it can be shown
that we can further reduce this number
to 20.*
Thus our curvature tensor,
for the situation in Relativity,
has only 20 components and NOT 256!

Now let us consider for a moment
the great IMPORTANCE of this tensor
in the study of spaces.

‡Thus in an ANTISYMMETRIC matrix we have

$$a_{\alpha\beta} = - a_{\beta\alpha},$$

whereas, in a SYMMETRIC matrix we have

$$a_{\alpha\beta} = a_{\beta\alpha}.$$

Note that if the first matrix on p. 208
were SYMMETRIC,
it would reduce to
TEN distinct elements,
since the elements in the principal diagonal
would NOT be zero in that case.
*See A. S. Eddington's
The Mathematical Theory of Relativity,
page 72 of the 1930 edition.

Suppose we have
a Euclidean space
of two, three, or more dimensions,
and suppose we use
ordinary rectangular coordinates.
Here the g's are all constants.*
Hence,
since the derivative of a constant
is zero
the Christoffel symbols will
also be zero (see page 200),
and, therefore,
all the components of the
curvature tensor
will be zero too,
because every term contains
a Christoffel symbol (see page 205).

BUT,
if the components of a tensor
in any given coordinate system
are all zero,
obviously its components in
any other coordinate system
would also be zero
(consider this in the simple case on page 129).

And so,
whereas from a mere superficial inspection
of the expression for ds^2
we cannot tell whether
the space is Euclidean or not,‡
an examination of the curvature tensor
(which of course is obtained
from the coefficients
in the expression for ds^2)

*See page 189.
‡See page 125.

210

can definitely give this information,
no matter what coordinate system
is used in setting up ds^2.
Thus,
whether we use (3) on page 116
or (7) or (8) on page 123 ,
all of which represent
the square of the distance
between two points
ON A EUCLIDEAN PLANE,
using various coordinate systems,
we shall find that
the components of $B^\alpha_{\sigma\tau\rho}$ in all three cases
ARE ALL ZERO.*
The same is true
for all coordinate systems
and for any number of dimensions,
provided that we remain in
Euclidean geometry.

*To have a clear idea of
 the meaning of the symbolism,
 the reader should try the simple exercise
 of showing that $B^\alpha_{\sigma\tau\rho} = 0$ for (8) on p. 123.
 He must bear in mind that here

$$g_{11} = 1 , \quad g_{12} = g_{21} = 0, \quad g_{22} = x_1^2 ,$$

and use these values in the bracketed expression
in (53) on page 205,
remembering of course that the meaning of $\{\sigma\rho , \epsilon\}$, etc.
is given by the definition on page 196;
also that all indices, σ , ρ , ϵ , etc.
have the possible values 1 and 2,
since the space here is
two-dimensional;
and he must not forget to SUM
whenever an index appears
TWICE IN ANY ONE TERM.

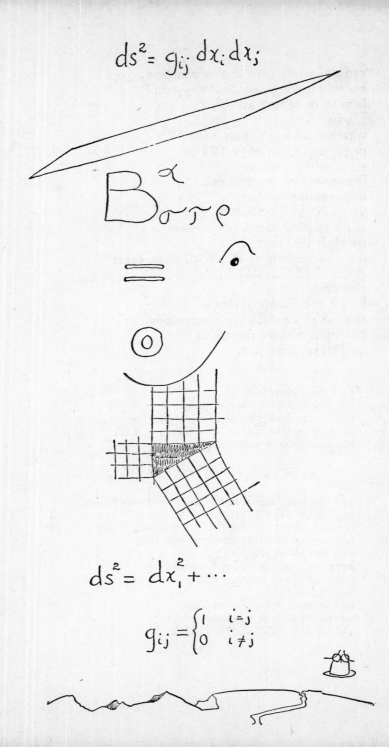

Thus

(54) $\qquad B^{\alpha}_{\sigma\tau\rho} = 0$

is a NECESSARY condition
that a space shall be
EUCLIDEAN.

It can be shown that
this is also a SUFFICIENT condition.

In other words,
given a Euclidean space,
this tensor will be zero,
whatever coordinate system is used,
AND CONVERSELY,
given this tensor equal to zero,
then we know that
the space must be Euclidean.

We shall now see
how the new Law of Gravitation
is EASILY derived
from this tensor.

XXV. THE BIG G'S OR EINSTEIN'S LAW OF GRAVITATION.

In (54) replace ρ by α,
obtaining

(55) $\qquad B^{\alpha}_{\sigma\tau\alpha} = 0.$

Since α appears twice
in the term on the left,
we must,
according to the usual convention,
sum on α,

213

so that (55) represents
only SIXTEEN equations
corresponding to the
4×4 values of σ and τ
in a four-dimensional continuum.
Thus, when $\sigma = \tau = 1$,
(55) becomes

$$B^1_{111} + B^2_{112} + B^3_{113} + B^4_{114} = 0.$$

Similarly for $\sigma = 1$, $\tau = 2$,
we get

$$B^1_{121} + B^2_{122} + B^3_{123} + B^4_{124} = 0$$

and so on,
for the 16 possible combinations of σ and τ.
We may therefore write (55) in the form

(56) $\qquad G_{\sigma\tau} = 0$

where each G consists of 4 B's
as shown above.
In other words,
by CONTRACTING $B^\alpha_{\sigma\tau\rho}$,
which is a tensor of the FOURTH rank,
we get a tensor of the SECOND rank,
namely, $G_{\sigma\tau}$,
as explained on page 182.

The QUITE INNOCENT-LOOKING
EQUATION (56) IS
EINSTEIN'S LAW OF GRAVITATION.

Perhaps the reader is startled
by this sudden announcement.
But let us look into (56)
carefully,
and see what is behind its
innocent simplicity,

215

and why it deserves to be called
the Law of Gravitation.

In the first place
it must be remembered
that before contraction,

$$B^{\alpha}_{\sigma\tau\rho}$$

represented the quantity in brackets
in the right-hand member
of equation (53) on page 205.
Hence,
when we contracted it
by replacing ρ by α,
we can see from (53) that
$G_{\sigma\tau}$ represents
the following expression:

$$(57) \quad \{\sigma\alpha, \epsilon\}\{\epsilon\tau, \alpha\} - \frac{\partial}{\partial x_{\alpha}}\{\sigma\tau, \alpha\} + \frac{\partial}{\partial x_{r}}\{\sigma\alpha, \alpha\}$$
$$- \{\sigma\tau, \epsilon\}\{\epsilon\alpha, \alpha\},$$

which, in turn,
by the definition of
the Christoffel symbol (page 196)
represents
an expression containing
first and second partial derivatives
of the little g's.
And, of course,
(57) takes 16 different values
as σ and τ each take on
their 4 different values,
while the other Greek letters in (57),
namely, α and ϵ,
are mere dummies (see page 204)
and are to be summed
(since each occurs twice in each term),
as usual.

To get clearly in mind
just what (57) means,
the reader is advised
to replace each Christoffel symbol
in accordance with the definition on page 196,
and to write out in particular
one of the 16 expressions represented by (57)
by putting, say $\sigma = 1$ and $\tau = 2$,
and allowing α and ϵ to assume,
in succession,
the values 1, 2, 3, 4.

It can easily be shown
that (56) actually represents
NOT 16 DIFFERENT equations
but only 10,
and, of these, only 6 are independent.*
So that the new Law of Gravitation
is not quite so complicated
as it appears at first.

But why do we call it a
Law of Gravitation at all?

It will be remembered
that a space,
of any number of dimensions,
is characterized by
its expression for ds^2 (see page 187).
Thus
(56) is completely determined by
the nature of the space which,
by the Principle of Equivalence
determines the path
of a freely moving object
in the space.

*See p. 242.

217

But, even granting the
Principle of Equivalence,
that is,
granting the idea
that the nature of the space,
rather than a "force" of gravity,
determines how objects (or light)
move in that space —
in other words,
granting that the g's alone
determine the Law of Gravitation —
one may still ask:
Why is this particular expression (56)
taken to be the
Law of Gravitation?

To which the answer is that
it is the SIMPLEST expression which is
ANALOGOUS to Newton's Law of Gravitation.
Perhaps the reader is unpleasantly surprised
at this reply,
and thinks that the choice has been
made rather ARBITRARILY!
May we therefore suggest to him
to read through the rest of this book
in order to find out
the CONSEQUENCES of Einstein's choice
of the Law of Gravitation.
We predict that he will be convinced
of the WISDOM of this choice,*
and will appreciate that this is
part of Einstein's GENIUS!

*The reader who is particularly
 interested in this point
 may wish to look up a book called
 "The Law of Gravitation in Relativity"
 by Levinson and Zeisler, 1931.

218

He will see, for example, on page 271 ,
that the equations giving
the path of a planet,
derived by Newton,
are the SAME, to a first approximation,
as the Einstein equations,
so that the latter can do
ALL that the Newtonian equations do,
and FURTHERMORE,
the ADDITIONAL term in (84)
accounts for the "unusual" path
of the planet Mercury,
which the Newtonian equation (85)
did not account for at all.
But we are anticipating the story!

Let us now express Newton's Law in
a form which will show the analogy clearly.

XXVI. COMPARISON OF EINSTEIN'S LAW OF GRAVITATION WITH NEWTON'S.

Everyone knows that,
according to Newton,*
two bodies attract each other
with a force which is proportional
to the product of their masses,
and inversely proportional to the
square of the distance between them,
thus:

$$F = \frac{km_1m_2}{r^2}.$$

*See the chapter on the
  "Theory of Attractive Forces" in
  Ziwet and Field's
  Introduction to Analytical Mechanics.

In this formula
we regard the two bodies,
of masses m_1 and m_2,
as each concentrated at a single point *
(its "center of gravity"),
and r is then precisely
the distance between these two points.
Now we may consider that m_1
is surrounded by a "gravitational field"
in which the gravitational force at A
(see the diagram on page 221)
is given by the above equation.
If we divide both sides by m_2
we get

$$\frac{F}{m_2} = \frac{km_1}{r^2} .$$

And, according to Newton,

$\dfrac{F}{m_2} = a$, the acceleration with which

m_2 would move due to
the force F acting on it.
We may therefore write

(58) $$a = \frac{C}{r^2}$$

where the constant C now includes m_1
since we are speaking of
the gravitational field around m_1.

*Thus it is a fact that
 to support a body
 it is not necessary to
 hold it up all over,
 but one needs only support it
 right under its center of gravity,
 as if its entire mass
 were concentrated at that point.

Now, acceleration is a vector quantity,*
and it may be split up into components:†
Thus take the origin to be at m_1,
and the mass m_2 at A:

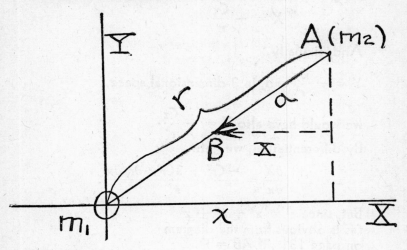

then $OA = r$;
and let AB represent the acceleration at A
(since m_2 is being pulled toward m_1)
in both magnitude and direction.
Now if X is the x-component of a,
it is obvious that

$$\frac{X}{a} = \frac{x}{r}.$$

Therefore

$$X = a \cdot \frac{x}{r}.$$

Or, better,

$$X = -a \cdot \frac{x}{r}$$

*See page 127.
†See page 129.

to show that the direction of X is to the left.
Substituting in this equation
the value of a from (58)
we get:

$$X = - \frac{Cx}{r^3}.$$

And, similarly,

$$Y = - \frac{Cy}{r^3} \text{ and, in 3-dimensional space,}$$

we would have also $Z = - \dfrac{Cz}{r^3}.$

By differentiation, we get:

$$\frac{\partial X}{\partial x} = \frac{-Cr^3 + 3Cr^2 x \cdot \partial r/\partial x}{r^6}.$$

But, since $r^2 = x^2 + y^2 + z^2$
(as is obvious from the diagram
on page 131 , if $AB = r$),

then $\qquad \dfrac{\partial r}{\partial x} = \dfrac{x}{r}.$

Substituting this in the above equation,
it becomes

$$\frac{\partial X}{\partial x} = \frac{-Cr^3 + 3Cx^2 r}{r^6} = \frac{-C(r^2 - 3x^2)}{r^5}.$$

And, similarly,

$$\frac{\partial Y}{\partial y} = \frac{-C(r^2 - 3y^2)}{r^5} \text{ and } \frac{\partial Z}{\partial z} = \frac{-C(r^2 - 3z^2)}{r^5}.$$

From these we get:

(59) $\qquad \dfrac{\partial X}{\partial x} + \dfrac{\partial Y}{\partial y} + \dfrac{\partial Z}{\partial z} = 0.$

This equation may be written:

(60)
$$\frac{\partial^2 \phi}{\partial x^2} + \frac{\partial^2 \phi}{\partial y^2} + \frac{\partial^2 \phi}{\partial z^2} = 0$$

where ϕ is a function such that

$$X = \frac{\partial \phi}{\partial x}, \ Y = \frac{\partial \phi}{\partial y}, \ Z = \frac{\partial \phi}{\partial z}$$

and is called the
"gravitational potential"; *
obviously (60) is merely another way
of expressing the field equation (59)
obtained from
Newton's Law of Gravitation.
This form of the law, namely (60),
is generally known as
the Laplace equation
and is more briefly denoted by

$$\nabla^2 \phi = 0$$

where the symbol ∇^2 merely denotes†
that
the second partial derivatives
with respect to x, y, and z,
respectively,
are to be taken and added together,
as shown in (60).
We see from (60), then,
that the gravitational field equation
obtained from
Newton's Law of Gravitation
is an equation containing
the second partial derivatives
of the gravitational potential.

* See footnote on page 219.
†The symbol ∇ is read "nabla",
  and ∇^2 is read "nabla square".

Whereas (56) is
a set of equations
which also contain
nothing higher than
the second partial derivatives
of the g's,
which,
by the Principle of Equivalence,
replace the notion of
a gravitational potential
derived from the idea of
a "force" of gravity,
by the idea of
the characteristic property of
the SPACE in question (see Ch. XII).
It is therefore reasonable
to accept (56) as the
gravitational field equations
which follow from the idea of
the Principle of Equivalence.

HOW REASONABLE it is
will be evident
when we test it by
EXPERIMENT!

It has been said (on page 215)
that each G consists of four B's.
Hence,
if the B's are all zero,
then the G's will all be zero;
but the converse
is obviously NOT true:
Namely,
even if the G's are all zero,
it does not necessarily follow
that the B's are zero.

225

But we know that,
to have the B's all zero
implies that
the space is Euclidean (see p. 213).

Thus,
if the condition for Euclidean space
is fulfilled,
namely,
$$B^\alpha_{\sigma\tau\rho} = 0 ,$$

then $G_{\sigma\tau} = 0$ automatically follows;
thus
$$G_{\sigma\tau} = 0$$

is true in the special case of
Euclidean space.
But, more than this,
since
$$G_{\sigma\tau} = 0$$

does NOT NECESSARILY imply
that the B's are zero,
hence
$$G_{\sigma\tau} = 0$$

can be true
EVEN IF THE SPACE IS
NOT EUCLIDEAN,
namely,
in the space around a body which
creates a gravitational field.

Now all this sounds very reasonable,
but still one naturally asks:
"How can this new
Law of Gravitation
be tested EXPERIMENTALLY?"

226

Einstein suggested several ways
in which it might be tested.
and,
as every child now knows,
when the experiments were
actually carried out,
his predictions were all fulfilled,
and caused a great stir
not only in the scientific world,
but penetrated even into
the daily news
the world over.

But doubtless the reader
would like to know
the details of these experiments,
and just how the above-mentioned
Law of Gravitation
is applied to them.

That is what we shall show next.

XXVII. HOW CAN THE EINSTEIN LAW OF GRAVITATION BE TESTED?

We have seen that

$$G_{\sigma\tau} = 0$$

represents Einstein's new
Law of Gravitation,
and consists of 6 equations
containing partial derivatives of
the little g's.*

*See pages 215 to 217.

In order to test this law
we must obviously substitute in it
the values of the g's which
actually apply in our physical world;
in other words,
we must know first
what is the expression for ds^2
which applies to our world
(see Chapter XIII).

Now, if we use
the customary polar coordinates,
we know that
in two-dimensional EUCLIDEAN space
we have

$$ds^2 = dr^2 + r^2 d\theta^2.*$$

Similarly,
for three-dimensional
EUCLIDEAN space
we have the well-known:

$$ds^2 = dr^2 + r^2 d\theta^2 + r^2 \sin^2\theta \cdot d\phi^2.$$

The reader can easily derive this from

$$ds^2 = dx_1^2 + dx_2^2 + dx_3^2 \text{ (on page 189),}$$

by changing to polar coordinates
with the aid of the diagram
on page 230.

*See page 123

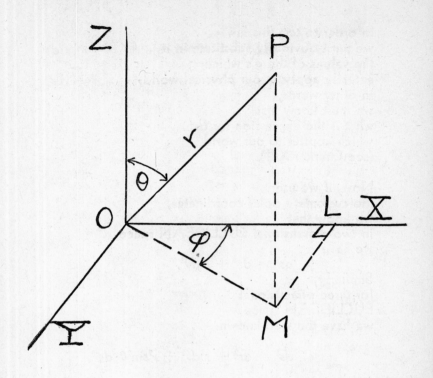

where
$$x_1 = x = OL = OM\cos \phi$$
$$= r \cos \angle POM \cos \phi = r \sin \theta \cos \phi$$
$$x_2 = y = LM = OM \sin \phi = r \sin \theta \sin \phi$$
$$x_3 = z = PM = r \cos \theta.$$

And,
for 4-dimensional space-time

we have

$$(61a)\begin{cases} ds^2 = -dr^2 - r^2d\theta^2 - r^2\sin^2d\theta \cdot d\phi^2 + c^2dt^2 \\ \text{or} \\ ds^2 = -dx_1^2 - x_1^2dx_2^2 - x_1^2\sin^2x_2 \cdot dx_3^2 + dx_4^2 \end{cases}$$

(where $x_1 = r$, $x_2 = \theta$, $x_3 = \phi$, $x_4 = t$, and c is taken equal to 1), as we can readily see:

Note that the general form for four-dimensional space in Cartesian coordinates, analogous to the 3-dimensional one on p. 189, is:

$$ds^2 = dx^2 + dy^2 + dz^2 + d\tau^2.$$

But, on page 67
we showed that
in order to get
the square of an "interval" in
space-time
in this form,
with all four plus signs,
we had to take τ NOT equal to
the time, t,
BUT to take $\tau = -ict$,* where

$i = \sqrt{-1}$, and
$c =$ the velocity of light;
from which

$$d\tau^2 = -c^2dt^2,$$

and the above expression becomes:

$$ds^2 = dx^2 + dy^2 + dz^2 - c^2dt^2.$$

*As a matter of fact,
in "Special Relativity,"
we took $\tau = -it$,
but that was because
we also took $c = 1$;
otherwise, we must take $\tau = -ict$.

And, furthermore,
since in actual fact,
c^2dt^2 is always found to be
greater than $(dx^2 + dy^2 + dz^2)$,
therefore,
to make ds come out real instead of imaginary,
it is more reasonable to write

$$ds^2 = -dx^2 - dy^2 - dz^2 + c^2dt^2,$$

which in polar coordinates,
becomes (61a).

The reader must clearly realize that
this formula still applies to
EUCLIDEAN space-time,
which is involved in
the SPECIAL theory of Relativity*
where we considered only
observers moving with
UNIFORM velocity relatively to each other.
But now,
in the GENERAL theory (page 96)
where we are considering
accelerated motion (page 102),
and therefore have a
NON-EUCLIDEAN space-time
(see Chapter XII),
what expression for ds^2
shall we use?

In the first place
it is reasonable to assume that

$$(61b) \quad ds^2 = -e^\lambda dx_1^2 - e^\mu (x_1^2 dx_2^2 + x_1^2 \sin^2 x_2 dx_3^2) + e^\nu dx_4^2.$$

(where x_1, x_2, x_3, x_4 represent

*See Part I of this book.

the polar coordinates r, θ, ϕ, and t,
respectively,
and λ, μ, and ν are functions of x_1 only),
BECAUSE:

(A) we do not include product terms
of the form $dx_1 \cdot dx_2$,
or, more generally,
of the form $dx_\sigma \, dx_\tau$ where $\sigma \neq \tau$,
(which ARE included in (42), p. 187)
since

from astronomical evidence
it seems that
our universe is
(a) ISOTROPIC and
(b) HOMOGENEOUS:
That is,
the distribution of matter
(the nebulae)
is the SAME
(a) IN ALL DIRECTIONS and
(b) FROM WHICHEVER POINT WE LOOK.

Now,
how does the omission of terms like

$$dx_\sigma \, dx_\tau \text{ where } \sigma \neq \tau$$

represent this mathematically?
Well, obviously,
a term like $dr \cdot d\theta$
(or $d\theta \cdot d\phi$ or $dr \cdot d\phi$)
would be different
for θ (or ϕ or r) positive or negative,
and, consequently,
the expression for ds^2
would be different if we turn
in opposite directions —

which would contradict the
experimental evidence that
the universe is ISOTROPIC.
And of course the use of
the same expression for ds^2
from ANY point
reflects the idea of HOMOGENEITY.
And so we see that it is reasonable
to have in (61b)
only terms involving $d\theta^2$, $d\phi^2$, dr^2,
in which it makes no difference
whether we substitute $+d\theta$ or $-d\theta$, etc.

Similarly,
since in getting a measure for ds^2,
we are considering
a STATIC condition,
and not one which is changing
from moment to moment,
we must therefore not include
terms which will have different values
for $+dt$ and $-dt$;
in other words,
we must not include
product terms like $dr \cdot dt$, etc.
In short

we must not have any terms involving

$$dx_\sigma \cdot dx_\tau \text{ where } \sigma \neq \tau,$$

but only terms involving

$$dx_\sigma \cdot dx_\tau \text{ where } \sigma = \tau.$$

(B) The factors e^λ, e^μ, e^ν, are inserted
   in the coefficients *
   to allow for the fact

*Cf. (61a) and (61b).

235

that our space is now
NON-EUCLIDEAN.
Hence they are so chosen as to
allow freedom to adjust them
to the actual physical world
(since they are variables),
and yet
their FORM is such that
it will be easy to manipulate them
in making the necessary adjustment —
as we shall see.*

Now,
(61b) can be somewhat simplified
by replacing

$$e^\mu x_1^2 \text{ by } (x_1')^2,$$

and taking x_1' as a new coordinate,
thus getting rid of e^μ entirely;
and we may even drop the prime,
since any change in dx_1^2 which arises
from the above substitution
can be taken care of
by taking λ correspondingly different.
Thus (61b) becomes, more simply,

$$\text{(62) } ds^2 = - e^\lambda dx_1^2 - x_1^2 dx_2^2 - x_1^2 \sin^2 x_2 dx_3^2 + e^\nu \cdot dx_4^2.$$

And we now have to find
the values of the coefficients

$$e^\lambda \text{ and } e^\nu$$

in terms of x_1.†

*Further justification for (61b)
 may be found in
 R. C. Tolman's
 Relativity Thermodynamics & Cosmology,
 p. 239 ff.
†See page 234.

We warn the reader that this is a
COLOSSAL UNDERTAKING,
but, in spite of this bad news,
we hasten to console him by
telling him that
many terms will reduce to zero,
and the whole complicated structure
will melt down to almost nothing;
we can then apply the result
to the physical data
with the greatest ease.
To any reader who "can't take it"
we suggest that
he omit the next chapter
and merely use the result
to follow
the experimental tests of the
Einstein Law of Gravitation
given from page 255 on.

BUT HE WILL MISS A LOT OF FUN!

XXVIII. SURMOUNTING THE DIFFICULTIES.

So far, then,
we have the following values:

$g_{11} = - e^{\lambda}$, $g_{22} = - x_1^2$, $g_{33} = - x_1^2 \sin^2 x_2$, $g_{44} = e^{\nu}$
and $g_{\sigma\tau} = 0$ when $\sigma \neq \tau$. (see (62) on p. 236.)
Furthermore,
the determinant g (see page 194)
is simply equal to
the product of the four elements in
its principal diagonal,

since all the other elements are zero:

$$\begin{vmatrix} -e^\lambda & 0 & 0 & 0 \\ 0 & -x_1^2 & 0 & 0 \\ 0 & 0 & -x_1^2\sin^2 x_2 & 0 \\ 0 & 0 & 0 & e^\nu \end{vmatrix}$$

Hence

$$g =_{,} - e^{\lambda+\nu} \cdot x_1^4 \sin^2 x_2 \,.^*$$

Also, in this case,

$$g^{\sigma\sigma} = 1/g_{\sigma\sigma}$$

and

$$g^{\sigma\tau} = 0 \text{ when } \sigma \neq \tau. \dagger$$

We shall need these relationships
in determining e^λ and e^ν in (62).

Now we shall see
how the big G's will help us to
find the little g's
and how the little g's will help us
to reduce the number of big G's to
ONLY THREE!

First let us show that
the set of quantities

$$G_{\sigma\tau}$$

is SYMMETRIC,‡
and therefore

*See the chapter on determinants
in any college algebra,
to find out how to evaluate
a determinant of the fourth order.
†See the definition of $g^{\mu\nu}$ on page 196.
‡See page 193.

239

$G_{\sigma\tau} = 0$ reduces to TEN equations *
instead of sixteen,
as σ and τ each take on
their values 1 , 2 , 3 , 4.
To show this,
we must remember that
$G_{\sigma\tau}$ really represents (57) on p. 216,
and let us examine $\{\sigma\alpha, \alpha\}$
which occurs in (57):
By definition (page 196),

$$\{\sigma\alpha, \alpha\} = \tfrac{1}{2}\, g^{\alpha\epsilon}\left(\frac{\partial g_{\sigma\epsilon}}{\partial x_\alpha} + \frac{\partial g_{\alpha\epsilon}}{\partial x_\sigma} - \frac{\partial g_{\sigma\alpha}}{\partial x_\epsilon}\right).$$

But,
remembering that
the presence of α and ϵ TWICE
in EACH term
(after multiplying out)
implies that we must SUM on α and ϵ,
the reader will easily see that
many of the terms will cancel out
and that we shall get

$$\{\sigma\alpha, \alpha\} = \tfrac{1}{2}\, g^{\alpha\epsilon} \frac{\partial g_{\alpha\epsilon}}{\partial x_\sigma}.$$

Furthermore,
by the definition of $g^{\mu\nu}$ on page 196,
the reader may also verify the fact that

$$\tfrac{1}{2}\, g^{\alpha\epsilon} \frac{\partial g_{\alpha\epsilon}}{\partial x_\sigma} = \frac{1}{2g} \cdot \frac{\partial g}{\partial x_\sigma}$$

where g is the determinant of p. 239.
And, from elementary calculus,

*See page 193.

$$\frac{1}{2g} \cdot \frac{\partial g}{\partial x_\sigma} = \frac{\partial}{\partial x_\sigma} \log \sqrt{-g}.^*$$

Hence,

$$\{\sigma\alpha, \alpha\} = \frac{\partial}{\partial x_\sigma} \log \sqrt{-g}.$$

Similarly,

$$\{\epsilon\alpha, \alpha\}' = \frac{\partial}{\partial x_\epsilon} \log \sqrt{-g}.$$

Substituting these values in (57),
we get:

(63) $\mathbf{G}_{\sigma\tau} \equiv \{\sigma\alpha, \epsilon\} \{\epsilon\tau, \alpha\} - \dfrac{\partial}{\partial x_\alpha} \{\sigma\tau, \alpha\} +$

$\dfrac{\partial^2}{\partial x_\sigma \cdot \partial x_\tau} \log \sqrt{-g} - \{\sigma\tau, \epsilon\} \dfrac{\partial}{\partial x_\epsilon} \log \sqrt{-g} = 0$

We can now easily see
that (63) represents
10 equations and not sixteen,
for the following reasons:
In the first place,

$$\{\epsilon\tau, \alpha\} = \{\tau\epsilon, \alpha\} \quad \text{(see pp. 204, 205)}.$$

Hence,
by interchanging σ and τ,
the first term of (63) remains unchanged,
its two factors merely change places

*Note that
we might also have obtained $\sqrt{+g}$,
but since g is always negative
(we shall show on p. 252 that $\lambda = -v$,
and therefore g on p. 239 becomes $-x_1^4 \cdot \sin^2 x_2$)
it is more reasonable to select $\sqrt{-g}$, which
will make the Christoffel symbols,
and hence also the terms in
the new Law of Gravitation,
REAL rather than imaginary.

241

(since ϵ and α are mere dummies,
as explained on page 204).
And,
the second, third and fourth terms of (63)
are also unchanged by
the interchange of σ and τ.
In other words,

$$G_{\sigma\tau} = G_{\tau\sigma}.$$

Thus, if we arrange
the 16 quantities in $G_{\sigma\tau}$
in a square array:

$$\left\|\begin{array}{cccc} G_{11} & G_{12} & G_{13} & G_{14} \\ G_{21} & G_{22} & G_{23} & G_{24} \\ G_{31} & G_{32} & G_{33} & G_{34} \\ G_{41} & G_{42} & G_{43} & G_{44} \end{array}\right\|$$

We have just shown that
this is a SYMMETRIC matrix.*
Hence (63) reduces to 10 equations
instead of 16,
as we said before.

We shall not burden the reader
with the details of
how (63) is further reduced
to only SIX equations.†
But perhaps the reader is thinking
that "only six" equations
are still no great consolation,
particularly if he realizes

*See page 239.
†If he is interested,
  he may look this up on page 115 of
  "The Mathematical Theory of Relativity,"
  by A. S. Eddington,
  the 1930 edition.

242

how long each of these equations is !
But does he realize this?
he would do well to take
particular values of σ and τ ,
say $\sigma = 1$, and $\tau = 1$,
in order to see just what
ONE of the equations in (63)
is really like!
(don't forget to sum on the dummies !)

Is the reader wondering
just what we are trying to do to him?
Is this a subtle mental torture
by which we
alternately frighten and console him?
The fact is that
we do want to frighten him sufficiently
to make him realize
the colossal amount of computation
that is involved here,
and yet to keep up his courage too
by the knowledge that
it does eventually boil down
to a really simple form.
He might not appreciate
the final simple form
if he did not know
the labor that produced it.
With this apology,
we shall now proceed to indicate
how the further simplification
takes place.

In each Christoffel symbol in (63),
we must substitute specific values
for the Greek letters.
It is obvious then

that there will be four possible types:

(a) those in which the values of
all three Greek letters are alike:
Thus: $\{\sigma\sigma\,,\,\sigma\}$

(b) those of the form $\{\sigma\sigma\,,\,\tau\}$
(c) those of the form $\{\sigma\tau\,,\,\tau\}$
and

(d) those of the form $\{\sigma\tau\,,\,\rho\}$.

Note that it is unnecessary to consider
the form $\{\tau\sigma\,,\,\tau\}$
since this is the same as $\{\sigma\tau\,,\,\tau\}$ (see p. 204).

Now, by definition (page 196),

$$\{\sigma\sigma\,,\,\sigma\} = \tfrac{1}{2}\,g^{\sigma\alpha}\left(\frac{\partial g_{\sigma\alpha}}{\partial x_\sigma} + \frac{\partial g_{\sigma\alpha}}{\partial x_\sigma} - \frac{\partial g_{\sigma\sigma}}{\partial x_\alpha}\right)$$

and, as usual,
we must sum on α.
But since the only g's which are not zero
are those in which
the indices are alike (see p. 237)
and, in that case,

$$g^{\sigma\sigma} = 1/g_{\sigma\sigma} \quad \text{(p. 239)}.$$

Hence

$$\{\sigma\sigma\,,\,\sigma\} = \frac{1}{2g_{\sigma\sigma}}\left(\frac{\partial g_{\sigma\sigma}}{\partial x_\sigma} + \frac{\partial g_{\sigma\sigma}}{\partial x_\sigma} - \frac{\partial g_{\sigma\sigma}}{\partial x_\sigma}\right)$$

and therefore

$$\{\sigma\sigma\,,\,\sigma\} = \frac{1}{2g_{\sigma\sigma}}\cdot\frac{\partial g_{\sigma\sigma}}{\partial x_\sigma}$$

which, by elementary calculus, gives

(a) $$\{\sigma\sigma\,,\,\sigma\} = \frac{1}{2}\frac{\partial}{\partial x_\sigma}\log g_{\sigma\sigma}.$$

Similarly,

$$\{\sigma\sigma,\tau\} = \frac{1}{2}\,g^{\tau\alpha}\left(\frac{\partial g_{\sigma\alpha}}{\partial x_\sigma} + \frac{\partial g_{\sigma\alpha}}{\partial x_\sigma} - \frac{\partial g_{\sigma\sigma}}{\partial x_\alpha}\right).$$

Here the only values of α that
will keep the outside factor $g^{\tau\alpha}$ from being zero
are those for which $\alpha = \tau$,
and since $\tau \neq \sigma$
(for otherwise we should have case (a))
we get

$$\{\sigma\sigma,\tau\} = -\frac{1}{2}\,g^{\tau\tau}\cdot\frac{\partial g_{\sigma\sigma}}{\partial x_\tau}$$

or

(b) $$\{\sigma\sigma,\tau\} = -\frac{1}{2g_{\tau\tau}}\cdot\frac{\partial g_{\sigma\sigma}}{\partial x_\tau}.$$

Likewise

(c) $$\{\sigma\tau,\tau\} = \frac{1}{2}\frac{\partial}{\partial x_\sigma}\,\log g_{\tau\tau}$$

and

(d) $$\{\sigma\tau,\rho\} = 0.$$

Let us now evaluate these various forms
for specific values:
Thus, take, in case (a), $\sigma = 1$:

Then $$\{11,1\} = \frac{1}{2}\cdot\frac{\partial}{\partial x_1}\,\log g_{11}$$

But $g_{11} = -e^\lambda$ (See p. 239).

hence $$\{11,1\} = \frac{1}{2}\cdot\frac{\partial}{\partial x_1}\,\log(-e^\lambda)$$

which, by elementary calculus, gives

$$\{11,1\} = \frac{1}{2}\left(\frac{-e^\lambda}{-e^\lambda}\right)\frac{\partial\lambda}{\partial x_1} = \frac{1}{2}\cdot\frac{\partial\lambda}{\partial x_1} = \frac{1}{2}\,\lambda',$$

245

where λ' represents $\dfrac{\partial \lambda}{\partial x_1}$ or $\dfrac{\partial \lambda}{\partial r}$,

since $x_1 = r$ (see page 233).

Similarly,
$$\{22, 2\} = \frac{1}{2} \cdot \frac{\partial}{\partial x_2} \log g_{22} = \frac{1}{2} \frac{\partial}{\partial x_2} \log(-x_1^2).$$

But, since
in taking a PARTIAL derivative
with respect to one variable,
all the other variables are held constant,
hence
$$\frac{\partial}{\partial x_2} \log(-x_1^2) = 0,$$

and therefore
$$\{22, 2\} = 0.$$

And, likewise,
$$\{33, 3\} = \{44, 4\} = 0.$$

Now, for case (b),
take first $\sigma = 1$, $\tau = 2$;
then
$$\{11, 2\} = -\frac{1}{2g_{22}} \cdot \frac{\partial}{\partial x_2} g_{11} = -\frac{1}{2g_{22}} \cdot \frac{\partial}{\partial x_2}(-e^\lambda).$$

But, since λ is a function of x_1 only,*
and is therefore held constant
while the partial derivative
with respect to x_2 is taken,
hence $\{11, 2\} = 0$,
and so on.

Let us see how many specific values
we shall have in all.
Obviously (a) has 4 specific cases,

*See page 234.

namely, $\sigma = 1 , 2 , 3 , 4 ,$
which have already been evaluated above.

(b) will have 12 specific cases,
since for each value of $\sigma = 1 , 2 , 3 , 4 ,$
τ can have 3 of its possible 4 values
(for here $\sigma \neq \tau$);

(c) will also have 12 cases,
and
(d) will have $4 \times 3 \times 2 = 24$ cases,
but since $\{\sigma\tau , \rho\} = \{\tau\sigma , \rho\}$ (see p. 204),
this reduces to 12.

Hence in all
there are 40 cases.

The reader should verify the fact that
31 of the 40 reduce to zero,
the 9 remaining ones being

$$
\begin{aligned}
\{ 11 , 1 \} &= \frac{1}{2} \lambda' . \\[2mm]
\{ 12 , 2 \} &= \frac{1}{r} \\[2mm]
\{ 13 , 3 \} &= \frac{1}{r} \\[2mm]
\{ 14 , 4 \} &= \frac{1}{2} \nu' \\[2mm]
\{ 22 , 1 \} &= -re^{-\lambda} \\[2mm]
\{ 23 , 3 \} &= \cot \theta \, {}^* \\[2mm]
\{ 33 , 1 \} &= -r \sin^2\theta e^{-\lambda} \\[2mm]
\{ 33 , 2 \} &= -\sin \theta \cdot \cos\theta \\[2mm]
\{ 44 , 1 \} &= \frac{1}{2} e^{\nu-\lambda} \cdot \nu'
\end{aligned}
$$

(64)

*Remember that $x_2 = \theta$: see page 233.

Note that $v' = \dfrac{\partial v}{\partial x_1} = \dfrac{\partial v}{\partial r}$.

Now, in (63),
when we give to the various Greek letters
their possible values,
we find that,
since so many of the Christoffel symbols
are equal to zero,
a great many (over 200) terms drop out!
And there remain now
only FIVE equations,
each with a much smaller number of terms.
These are written out in full below,
and,
lest the reader think that
this is the promised
final simplified result,
we hasten to add that
the BEST is yet to come!

Just how G_{11} is obtained,
showing the reader how
to SUM on α and ϵ
and which terms drop out
(because they contain zero factors)
will be found in V,
on page 317.
And,
similarly for the other G's.
Here we give
the equations which result
after the zero terms have been
eliminated.

$$G_{11} = \{11,1\}\{11,1\} + \{12,2\}\{21,2\}+$$
$$\{13,3\}\{31,3\} + \{14,4\}\{41,4\}$$
$$- \frac{\partial}{\partial x_1}\{11,1\} + \frac{\partial^2}{\partial x_1^2}\log\sqrt{-g}$$
$$- \{11,1\}\frac{\partial}{\partial x_1}\log\sqrt{-g}$$
$$= 0.$$

Similarly,

$$G_{22} = 2\{22,1\}\{12,2\} + \{23,3\}\{23,3\}$$
$$- \frac{\partial}{\partial x_1}\{22,1\} + \frac{\partial^2}{\partial x_2^2}\log\sqrt{-g}$$
$$- \{22,1\}\frac{\partial}{\partial x_1}\log\sqrt{-g}$$
$$= 0.$$

$$G_{33} = 2\{33,1\}\{13,3\} + 2\{33,2\}\{23,3\}$$
$$- \frac{\partial}{\partial x_1}\{33,1\} - \frac{\partial}{\partial x_2}\{33,2\}$$
$$- \{33,1\}\frac{\partial}{\partial x_1}\log\sqrt{-g}$$
$$- \{33,2\}\frac{\partial}{\partial x_2}\log\sqrt{-g}$$
$$= 0.$$

$$G_{44} = 2\{44,1\}\{14,4\} - \frac{\partial}{\partial x_1}\{44,1\}$$
$$- \{44,1\}\frac{\partial}{\partial x_1}\log\sqrt{-g}$$
$$= 0.$$

$$G_{12} = \{13,3\}\{23,3\} - \{12,2\}\frac{\partial}{\partial x_2}\log\sqrt{-g}$$
$$= 0.$$

If we now substitute
in these equations
the values given in (64),
we get

$$G_{11} = \frac{1}{4}\lambda'^2 + \frac{1}{r^2} + \frac{1}{r^2} + \frac{1}{4}\nu'^2 - \frac{1}{2}\lambda'' + \left(\frac{1}{2}\lambda''\right.$$

$$+ \frac{1}{2}\nu'' - \frac{2}{r^2}\right) - \frac{1}{2}\lambda'\left(\frac{1}{2}\lambda' + \frac{1}{2}\nu' + \frac{2}{r}\right)$$

$$= \frac{1}{4}\nu'^2 + \frac{1}{2}\nu'' - \frac{1}{4}\lambda'\nu' - \frac{\lambda'}{r}$$

$$= 0^*$$

Similarly

$$G_{22} = e^{-\lambda}\left[1 + \frac{1}{2}r(\nu' - \lambda')\right] - 1 = 0.$$

$$G_{33} = \sin^2\theta \cdot e^{-\lambda}\left[1 + \frac{1}{2}r(\nu' - \lambda')\right] - \sin^2\theta$$

$$= 0.$$

$$G_{44} = e^{\nu-\lambda}\left(-\frac{1}{2}\nu'' + \frac{1}{4}\lambda'\nu' - \frac{1}{4}\nu'^2 - \frac{\nu'}{r}\right)$$

$$= 0.$$

*Here $\lambda'' = \dfrac{\partial^2 \lambda}{\partial r^2}$

and $\nu'' = \dfrac{\partial^2 \nu}{\partial r^2}$

and G_{12} becomes:

$$\frac{1}{r} \cot\theta - \frac{1}{r} \cot\theta = 0$$

which is identically zero
and therefore drops out,
thus reducing the number of equations
to FOUR.

Note also that
G_{33} includes G_{22},
so that these two equations
are not independent —
hence now the equations are
THREE.

And now, dividing G_{44} by $e^{\nu-\lambda}$
and adding the result to G_{11},
we get

(65) $\qquad \lambda' = -\nu'$

or $\qquad \dfrac{\partial\lambda}{\partial r} = -\dfrac{\partial\nu}{\partial r}.$

Therefore, by integration,

(66) $\qquad \lambda = -\nu + I$

where I is a constant of integration.

But, since
at an infinite distance from matter,
our universe would be Euclidean,*

*See page 226.

and then, for Cartesian coordinates,
we would have:

$$ds^2 = dx_1^2 + dx_2^2 + dx_3^2 + dx_4^2,*$$

that is,
the coefficient of dx_1^2 and of dx_4^2
must be 1 under these conditions;
hence,
if (61b) is to hold also for
this special case,
as of course it must do,
we should then have $\lambda = 0$, $\nu = 0$.

In other words,
since,
when $\nu = 0$, λ also equals 0 ,
then, from (66), l , too, must be zero.
Hence

(67) $\lambda = -\nu$.

Using (65) and (67),
G_{22} on page 250 becomes

(68) $e^\nu (1 + r\nu') = 1.$

If we put $\gamma = e^\nu$,
and differentiate with respect to r ,
we get

$$\frac{\partial \gamma}{\partial r} = e^\nu \cdot \frac{\partial \nu}{\partial r}$$

or

$$\gamma' = e^\nu \cdot \nu'.$$

Hence (68) becomes

(69) $\gamma + r\gamma' = 1.$

*See pages 189 and 231.

252

This equation may now be
easily integrated,*
obtaining

$$(70) \qquad \gamma = 1 - \frac{2m}{r}$$

where $2m$ is a constant of integration.
The constant m will later be shown
to have an important physical meaning.

Thus we have succeeded in finding

$$e^\lambda \text{ and } e^\nu$$

*From elementary theory of
 differential equations,
 we write (69):

$$\gamma + r\frac{d\gamma}{dr} = 1$$

or

$$r\frac{d\gamma}{dr} = 1 - \gamma$$

or

$$-\frac{d\gamma}{1-\gamma} = \frac{-dr}{r}.$$

Having separated the variables,
we can now integrate both sides
thus:

$$\log(1 - \gamma) = -\log r + \text{constant};$$

or

$$\log r(1 - \gamma) = \text{constant},$$

and therefore

$$r(1 - \gamma) = \text{constant}.$$

We may then write

$$r(1 - \gamma) = 2m,$$

from which we get

$$\gamma = 1 - \frac{2m}{r}.$$

in terms of x_1 :

$$e^{\nu} = 1/e^{\lambda} = \gamma = 1 - 2m/r = 1 - 2m/x_1$$

and (62) becomes:

$$(71) \quad ds^2 = - \gamma^{-1}dr^2 - r^2d\theta^2 - r^2\sin^2\theta \cdot d\phi^2 + \gamma dt^2,$$

where, as before (p. 233),

$$r = x_1, \quad \theta = x_2, \quad \phi = x_3, \quad t = x_4.$$

And hence
the new Law of Gravitation,
consisting now of only
the THREE remaining equations:

$$G_{11} = 0, G_{33} = 0, \text{ and } G_{44} = 0,$$

are now fully determined by
the little g's of (71).

We can now proceed
to test this result
to see whether it really applies
to the physical world we live in.

XXIX. "THE PROOF OF THE PUDDING."

The first test is naturally
to see what
the new Law of Gravitation
has to say about
the path of a planet.
It was assumed by Newton that
a body "naturally" moves
along a straight line

255

if it is not pulled out of its course
by some force acting on it:
As, for example,
a body moving on
a frictionless Euclidean plane.
Similarly,
according to Einstein
if it moves "freely" on
the surface of a SPHERE
it would go along the
"nearest thing to a straight line,"
that is,
along the GEODESIC for this surface,
namely,
along a great circle.
And, for other surfaces,
or spaces of higher dimensions,
it would move along
the corresponding geodesic for
the particular surface or space.

Now our problem is
to find out
what is the geodesic in
our non-Euclidean physical world,
since a planet must move
along such a geodesic.

In order to find
the equation of a geodesic
it is necessary to know
something about the
"Calculus of Variations,"
so that we cannot go into details here.
But we shall give the reader
a rough idea of the plan,
together with references where

he may look up this matter further.*
Suppose, for example, that
we have given
two points, *A* and *B* , on a
Euclidean plane;
it is obviously possible to
join them by various paths,
thus:

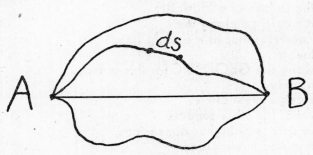

Now,
which of all possible paths
is the geodesic here?
Of course the reader knows the answer:
It is the straight line path.
But how do we set up
the problem mathematically
so that we may solve
similar problems in other cases?

*(1) For fundamental methods see
"Calculus of Variations," by
G. A. Bliss.
(2) For this specific problem see
"The Mathematical Theory of
Relativity," by A. S. Eddington,
p. 59 of the 1930 edition.
(3) Or see pages 128-134 of
"The Absolute Differential Calculus,"
by T. Levi-Civita.

Well,
we know from ordinary calculus
that
if a short arc on
any of these paths
is represented by *ds*,
then

$$\int_A^B ds$$

represents the total length of
that entire path.
And this of course applies to
any one of the paths from *A* to *B*.
How do we now select from among these
the geodesic?

This problem is similar to
one with which the reader is
undoubtedly familiar,
namely,

if $y = f(x)$,
find the values of *y* for which
y is an "extremum" or a "stationary."

Such values of *y* are shown in
the diagram on the next page
at *a*, *b*, and *c*:

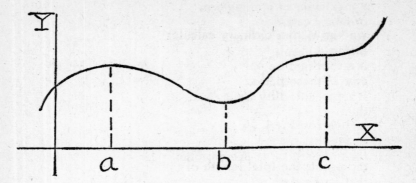

and, for all these, we must have
$$dy/dx = 0$$
or

(72) $$dy = f'(x_o) \cdot dx = 0$$

where x_o is a, b, or c.

Similarly,
to go back to our problem on pp. 258 and 259,
the geodesic we are looking for
would make

$$\int_A^B ds$$

a stationary.
This is expressed in
the calculus of variations by

(73) $$\delta \int_A^B ds = 0$$

analogously to (72).

To find the equation of the geodesic,
satisfying (73),
is not as simple as finding

a maximum or minimum in
ordinary calculus,
and we shall give here
only the result:*

(74) $$\frac{d^2x_\sigma}{ds^2} + \{\alpha\beta\,,\sigma\}\,\frac{dx_\alpha}{ds}\cdot\frac{dx_\beta}{ds} = 0$$

Let us consider (74):
In the first place,
for ordinary three-dimensional
Euclidean space
σ would have
three possible values: 1 , 2 , 3 ,
since we have here
three coordinates x_1, x_2, x_3;
furthermore,
by choosing Cartesian coordinates,
we would have (see page 189):

$$g_{11} = g_{22} = g_{33} = 1$$

and

$$g_{\mu\nu} = 0 \quad \text{for} \quad \mu \neq \nu\,,$$

and therefore

$$\{\alpha\beta\,,\sigma\}$$

which involves derivatives of the g's†
would be equal to zero,
so that (74) would become

(75) $$\frac{d^2x_\sigma}{ds^2} = 0 \qquad\qquad (\sigma = 1\,,2\,,3).$$

*For details, look up the references in
 the footnote on p. 258.
†See (46) on p. 196.

Now, if in (75)
we replace ds by dt, *
it becomes

(76) $\qquad \dfrac{d^2x_\sigma}{dt^2} = 0$ $\qquad\qquad$ ($\sigma = 1, 2, 3$)

which is a short way of writing
the three equations:

(77) $\quad \dfrac{d^2x_1}{dt^2} = 0$, $\quad \dfrac{d^2x_2}{dt^2} = 0$, $\quad \dfrac{d^2x_3}{dt^2} = 0.$

But what is
the PHYSICAL MEANING of (77)?

*If we consider an observer who
has chosen his coordinates
in such a way that

$$dx_1 = dx_2 = dx_3 = o,$$

in other words,
an observer who is traveling with
a moving object,
and for whom the object is therefore
standing still with reference to
his ordinary space-coordinates,
so that only time is changing for him,
then, for him (61a) becomes

$$ds^2 = dx_4^2$$

or $\qquad ds^2 = dt^2$

or $\qquad ds = dt.$

That is to say,
ds becomes of the nature of "time;"
for this reason
ds is often called
"the proper time"
since it is a "time"
for the moving object itself.

262

Why, everyone knows that,
for uniform motion,

$$v = s/t,$$

where v is the velocity with which
a body moves when
it goes a distance of s feet in
t seconds.
If the motion is NOT uniform,
we can, by means of
elementary differential calculus,
express the velocity AT AN INSTANT,
by

$$v = ds/dt.$$

Or, if x, y, and z are
the projections of s on the
X, Y, and Z axes, respectively,
and v_x, v_y, and v_z are
the projections of v
on the three axes,
then

$$v_x = \frac{dx}{dt}, \quad v_y = \frac{dy}{dt}, \quad v_z = \frac{dz}{dt}.$$

Or,
in the abridged notation,

$$v_\sigma = \frac{dx_\sigma}{dt} \qquad\qquad (\sigma = 1, 2, 3)$$

where we use x_1, x_2, x_3
instead of x, y, z,
and v_1, v_2, v_3 instead of v_x, v_y, v_z.

Furthermore,
since acceleration is
the change in velocity per unit of time,

263

we have
$$a = \frac{dv}{dt} \text{ or } a = \frac{d^2s}{dt^2}$$

or

(78)
$$a_\sigma = \frac{d^2x_\sigma}{dt^2} \qquad (\sigma = 1\,,\,2\,,\,3).$$

Thus (77) states that
the components of the acceleration
must be zero,
and hence the acceleration itself
must be zero, thus:
$$a = \frac{d^2s}{dt^2} = 0$$

or

$$a = \frac{dv}{dt} = 0.$$

From this we get, by integrating,
$$v = \text{a constant,}$$
or
$$\frac{ds}{dt} = \text{a constant,}$$

and therefore
by integrating again,
$$s = at + b,$$

which is the equation of
A STRAIGHT LINE.

In other words,
when the equations for a geodesic,
namely, (74),
are applied to the special case of
THREE-DIMENSIONAL EUCLIDEAN SPACE,
they lead to the fact that

264

in this special case
THE GEODESIC IS A STRAIGHT LINE!

We hope the reader is DELIGHTED
and NOT DISAPPOINTED
to get a result which is
so familiar to him;
and we hope it gives him
a friendly feeling of confidence
in (74)!
And of course he must realize
that (74) will work also
for any non-Euclidean space,
since it contains
the little g's
which characterize the space;*
and for any dimensionality,
since σ may be given
any number of values.

In particular,
in our four-dimensional
non-Euclidean world,
(74) represents
the path of an object moving
in the presence of matter
(which merely makes the space
non-Euclidean),
with no external force acting upon the object;
and hence (74) is
THE PATH OF A PLANET
which we are looking for!

*See p. 190.

XXX. MORE ABOUT THE PATH OF A PLANET.

Of course (74) is only
a GENERAL expression,
and does not yet apply to
our particular physical world,
since the Christoffel symbol

$$\{\alpha\beta \,,\, \sigma\}$$

involves the g's,
and is therefore not specific until
we substitute the values of the g's
which apply in a specific case
in the physical world.

Now in (64)
we have the values of $\{\alpha\beta \,,\, \sigma\}$
in terms of $\lambda \,,\, \nu \,,\, r$ and θ.
And, by (67), $\lambda = - \nu$,
hence we know $\{\alpha\beta \,,\, \sigma\}$ in terms of
$\nu \,,\, r$ and θ.
Further, since $e^{\nu} = \gamma$ (see page 252)
and γ is known in terms of r from (70),
we therefore have $\{\alpha\beta \,,\, \sigma\}$ in terms of

r and θ.

The reader must bear in mind
that
whereas (76), in Newtonian physics,
represents only three equations,
on the other hand,
(74) in Einsteinian physics
is an abridged notation for
FOUR equations,

266

as σ takes on
its FOUR possible values: 1 , 2 , 3 , 4.
Taking first the value $\sigma = 2$,
and, remembering that $x_2 = \theta$ (see page 233),
we have,
for one of the equations of (74),
the following:

$$(79) \qquad \frac{d^2\theta}{ds^2} + \{\alpha\beta , \sigma\} \frac{dx_\alpha}{ds} \cdot \frac{dx_\beta}{ds} = 0.$$

And now,
since α and β each occur
TWICE
in the second term,
we must sum on these as usual,
so that we must consider terms
containing, respectively,

$$\{11 , 2\}, \{12 , 2\}, \{13 , 2\}, \{14 , 2\},$$
$$\{21 , 2\}, \{22 , 2\}, \{23 , 2\}, \{24 , 2\}, \text{etc.}$$

in which σ always equals 2 ,
and α and β each runs its course
from 1 to 4.
But, from (64), we see that
most of these are zero,
the only ones remaining being

$$\{12 , 2\} = \frac{1}{r}$$

and

$$\{33 , 2\} = -\sin\theta \cdot \cos\theta.$$

Also, by page 204,

$$\{21 , 2\} = \{12 , 2\}.$$

267

Thus (79) becomes

(80) $$\frac{d^2\theta}{ds^2} + \frac{2}{r}\cdot\frac{dr}{ds}\cdot\frac{d\theta}{ds} - \sin\theta\cdot\cos\theta\left(\frac{d\phi}{ds}\right)^2 = 0.$$

If we now choose our coordinates
in such a way
that
an object begins moving in the plane

$$\theta = \pi/2\ ,$$

then

$$\frac{d\theta}{ds} = 0 \text{ and } \cos\theta = 0$$

and hence

$$\frac{d^2\theta}{ds^2} = 0.$$

If we now substitute all these values in (80),
we see that this equation is satisfied,
and hence $\theta = \pi/2$ is a solution of the equation,
thus showing that
the path of the planet
is in a plane.

Thus from (80)
we have found out that
a planet,
according to Einstein,
must move in a plane,
just as in Newtonian physics.

Let us now examine (74) further,
and see what
the 3 remaining equations in it
tell us about planetary motion:

268

For $\sigma = 1$,
(79) becomes

$$\frac{d^2x_1}{ds^2} + \{11,1\}\left(\frac{dx_1}{ds}\right)^2 + \{22,1\}\left(\frac{dx_2}{ds}\right)^2$$
$$+ \{33,1\}\left(\frac{dx_3}{ds}\right)^2 + \{44,1\}\left(\frac{dx_4}{ds}\right)^2 = 0.$$

Or

$$\frac{d^2r}{ds^2} + \frac{1}{2}\lambda'\left(\frac{dr}{ds}\right)^2 - re^{-\lambda}\left(\frac{d\theta}{ds}\right)^2 - r\cdot\sin^2\theta\cdot e^{-\lambda}\left(\frac{d\phi}{ds}\right)^2$$
$$+ \frac{1}{2}e^{\nu-\lambda}\cdot\nu'\left(\frac{dt}{ds}\right)^2 = 0.$$

But since we have chosen $\theta = \pi/2$,
then

$$\frac{d\theta}{ds} = 0 \text{ and } \sin\theta = 1,$$

hence this equation becomes

$$(81) \qquad \frac{d^2r}{ds^2} + \frac{1}{2}\lambda'\left(\frac{dr}{ds}\right)^2 - re^{-\lambda}\left(\frac{d\phi}{ds}\right)^2$$
$$+ \frac{1}{2}e^{\nu-\lambda}\cdot\nu'\left(\frac{dt}{ds}\right)^2 = 0.$$

And similarly,
for $\sigma = 3$,
(79) gives

$$(82) \qquad \frac{d^2\phi}{ds^2} + \frac{2}{r}\cdot\frac{dr}{ds}\cdot\frac{d\phi}{ds} = 0,$$

and for $\sigma = 4$,
we get

$$(83) \qquad \frac{d^2t}{ds^2} + \nu'\frac{dr}{ds}\cdot\frac{dt}{ds} = 0.$$

269

And now
from (81), (82), (83), and (71),
together with (70),
we get*

$$(84) \quad \begin{cases} \dfrac{d^2u}{d\phi^2} + u = \dfrac{m}{h^2} + 3mu^2 \\[2ex] \quad\quad r^2 \dfrac{d\phi}{ds} = h \end{cases}$$

where c and h are
constants of integration,
and $u = 1/r$.

Thus (84) represents
the path of an object moving freely,
that is,
not constrained by any external force,
and is therefore,
in a sense,
analogous to a straight line in
Newtonian physics.
But it must be remembered
that in Einsteinian physics,
owing to the
Principle of Equivalence (Chapter XI),
an object is
NOT constrained by any external force
even when it is moving in
the presence of matter,
as, for example,
a planet moving
around the sun.
And hence (84)
would represent the path of a planet.

*For details see page 86 in
"The Mathematical Theory of Relativity," by
A. S. Eddington (the 1930 edition).

From this point of view
we are not interested in
comparing (84) with
the straight line motion in
Newtonian physics,
as mentioned on page 270,
but rather with
the equations representing
the path of a planet
in Newtonian physics,
in which, of course,
the planet is supposed to move
under the
GRAVITATIONAL FORCE
of the sun.
It has been shown
in Newtonian physics
that a body
moving under a "central force,"
(like a planet moving
under the influence of the sun)
moves in an ellipse,
with the central force (the sun)
located at one of the foci.*

And the equations of this path are:

$$(85) \quad \begin{cases} \dfrac{d^2u}{d\phi^2} + u = \dfrac{m}{h^2} \\ r^2 \dfrac{d\phi}{dt} = h \end{cases}$$

where r is the distance
from the sun to the planet,
m is the mass of the sun,

*See Ziwet and Field: "Mechanics,"
or any other book on mechanics.

a is the semi-major-axis of the ellipse,
ϕ is the angle swept out by the planet
in time *t*.

We notice at once
the remarkable resemblance between
(84) and (85).
They are indeed
IDENTICAL EXCEPT for
the presence of the term $3mu^2$,
and of course the use of
ds instead of *dt* in (84).*

Thus we see that
the Newtonian equations (85)
are really
a first approximation to
the Einstein equations (84);
that is why
they worked so satisfactorily
for so long.

Let us now see
how the situation is affected by
the additional term $3mu^2$.

XXXI. THE PERIHELION OF MERCURY.

Owing to the presence of the term
$$3mu^2$$
(84) is no longer an ellipse
but a kind of spiral
in which the path
is NOT retraced
each time the planet

*See p. 262.

272

makes a complete revolution,
but is shifted as shown
in the following diagram:

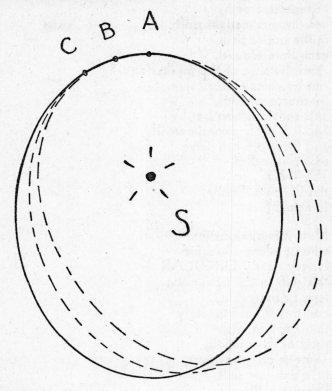

in which
the "perihelion," that is,
the point in the path
nearest the sun, S, at the focus,
is at A the first time around,
at B the next time,
at C the next,
and so on.

273

In other words,
a planet does not go
round and round
in the same path,
but there is a slight shift
in the entire path,
each time around.
And the shift of the perihelion
can be calculated
by means of (84).*
This shift can also be
MEASURED experimentally,
and therefore can serve
as a method of
TESTING
the Einstein theory
in actual fact.

Now it is obvious that
when a planetary orbit
is very nearly CIRCULAR
this shift in the perihelion
is not observable,
and this is unfortunately
the situation with
most of the planets.
There is one, however,
in which this shift
IS measurable,
namely,
the planet MERCURY.

Lest the reader think
that the astronomers

*For details see again
 Eddington's book referred to
 in the footnote of page 270.

can make only
crude measurements,
let us say in their defense,
that the discrepancy
even in the case of Mercury
is an arc of
ONLY ABOUT
43 SECONDS PER CENTURY!

Let us make clear what we mean by
"the discrepancy:"
when we say that
the Newtonian theory
requires the path of a planet to be
an ellipse,
it must be understood that
this would hold only if
there were a SINGLE planet;
the presence of other planets
causes so-called "perturbations,"
so that
even according to Newton
there would be
some shift in the
perihelion.
But the amount of shift
due to this cause
has long been known to be
531 seconds of arc per century,
whereas observation shows
that the actual shift is
574 seconds,
thus leaving a shift of
43 seconds per century
UNACCOUNTED FOR
in the Newtonian theory.

Think of the DELICACY

of the measurements
and the patient persistence
over a long period of years
by generations of astronomers
that is represented
by the above figure!
And this figure was known
to astronomers
long before Einstein.
It worried them deeply
since they could not account
for the presence of this shift.

And then
the Einstein theory,
which originated in the attempt
to explain
the Michelson-Morley experiment,*
and NOT AT ALL with the intention
of explaining the shift
in the perihelion of Mercury,
QUITE INCIDENTALLY EXPLAINED
THIS DIFFICULTY ALSO,
for the presence of the term $3mu^2$ in (84)
leads to the additional shift of perihelion
of 42.9'' ! †

XXXII. DEFLECTION OF A RAY OF LIGHT.

We saw in the previous chapter
that the experimental evidence

*See Part I.: the Special Theory of Relativity.
†For the details of the calculation which leads
from (84) to this correction of perihelion shift,
see p. 88 of the 1930 edition of
"The Mathematical Theory of Relativity," by
A. S. Eddington.

in connection with
the shift of the perihelion of Mercury
was already at hand
when Einstein's theory was proposed,
and immediately served
as a check of the theory.

Let us now consider
further experimental verification
of the theory, —
but this time
the evidence did not precede
but was PREDICTED BY
the theory.

This was in connection with
the path of a ray of light
as it passes near a large mass
like the sun.

It will be remembered that
according to the Einstein theory
the presence of matter in space
makes the space non-Euclidean
and that the path of anything moving freely
(whether it be a planet
or a ray of light)
will be along a geodesic
in that space, and therefore
will be affected by the presence
of these obstacles in space.
Whereas,
according to classical physics,
the force of gravitation
could be exerted
only by one mass (say the sun)
upon another mass (say a planet),
but NOT upon a ray of light.

Here then was
a definite difference in viewpoint
between the two theories,
and the facts should
decide between them.
For this it was necessary
to observe
what happens to a ray of light
coming from a distant star
as it passes near the sun —
is it bent toward the sun,
as predicted by Einstein,
or does it continue on
in a straight line,
as required by classical physics? *
Now it is obviously impossible
to make this observation
under ordinary circumstances,
since we cannot look at a star
whose rays are passing near the sun,
on account of the brightness of the sun itself:
Not only would the star be invisible,
but the glare of the sun
would make it impossible
to look in that direction at all.

And so it was necessary
to wait for a total eclipse,

*If, however, light were considered
  to be a stream of incandescent particles
  instead of waves,
  the sun WOULD have
  a gravitational effect upon
  a ray of light, even by classical theory,
  BUT,
  the AMOUNT of deflection
  calculated even on this basis,
  DOES NOT AGREE with experiment,
  as we shall show later (see p. 287).

when the sun is up in the sky
but its glare is hidden by the moon,
so that the stars become
distinctly visible during the day.
Therefore, at the next total eclipse
astronomical expeditions were sent out
to those parts of the world
where the eclipse could be
advantageously observed,
and, —
since such an eclipse
lasts only a few seconds, —
they had to be prepared
to take photographs of the stars
rapidly and clearly,
so that afterwards,
upon developing the plates,
the positions of the stars
could be compared
with their positions in the sky
when the sun is NOT present.

The following diagram shows

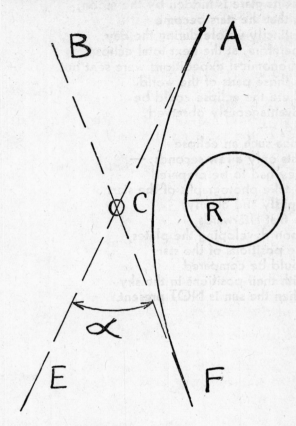

the path of a ray of light, *AOE*,
from a star, *A*,
when the sun is NOT
in that part of the sky.
And, also,
when the sun IS present,
and the ray is deflected
and becomes *ACF*,

so that,
when viewed from *F* ,
the star APPEARS to be at *B.*

Thus,
if such photographs
could be successfully obtained,
AND IF they showed
that all the stars
in the part of the sky near the sun
were really displaced (as from *A* to *B*)
AND IF
the MAGNITUDE of the displacements
agreed with the values
calculated by the theory,
then of course
this would constitute
very strong evidence in favor of
the Einstein theory.

Let us now determine
the magnitude of this displacement
as predicted by the Einstein theory:

We have seen (on page 233)
that
in the "Special Theory of Relativity,"
which applies in EUCLIDEAN space-time,

$$ds^2 = c^2 dt^2 - (dx^2 + dy^2 + dz^2);$$

if we now divide this expression by dt^2,
we get

$$\left(\frac{ds}{dt}\right)^2 = c^2 - \left[\left(\frac{dx}{dt}\right)^2 + \left(\frac{dy}{dt}\right)^2 + \left(\frac{dz}{dt}\right)^2\right],$$

but

since $\dfrac{dx}{dt}, \dfrac{dy}{dt}, \dfrac{dz}{dt}$ are

the components of the velocity, v, of
a moving thing (see p. 263),
then obviously the
above quantity in brackets is v^2,
and the above equation becomes:

$$\left(\frac{ds}{dt}\right)^2 = c^2 - v^2.$$

Now when
the "moving thing" happens to be
a light-ray,
then $v = c$,
and we get, FOR LIGHT,

$$ds = 0.$$

but what about our
NON-EUCLIDEAN world,
containing matter?

It will be remembered (see p. 118)
that in studying a
non-Euclidean two-dimensional space
(namely, the surface of a sphere)
in a certain small region,
we were aided by
the Euclidean plane which
practically coincided with
the given surface in
that small region.
Using the same device for
space of higher dimensions,
we can,
in studying a small region of
NON-Euclidean four-dimensional space-time,
such as our world is,
also utilize the
EUCLIDEAN 4-dimensional space-time which

practically coincides with it
in that small region.
And hence

$$ds = 0$$

will apply FOR LIGHT even
in our NON-EUCLIDEAN world.

And now,
using this result in (71),
together with the condition for
a geodesic, on page 261,
we shall obtain
THE PATH OF A RAY OF LIGHT.

XXXIII. DEFLECTION OF A RAY OF LIGHT — (Continued)

In chapters XXIX and XXX we showed that
the condition for a geodesic
given on page 260
led to (74),
which, together with
the little g's of (71)
gave us the path of a planet, (84).

And now,
in order to find
the path of A RAY OF LIGHT,
we must add the further requirement:

$$ds = 0 ,$$

as we pointed out in Chapter XXXII.
Substituting $ds = 0$ in
the second equation of (84),

we get
$$h = \infty \, ,$$

which changes the
first equation of (84) to

$$\frac{d^2u}{d\phi^2} + u = 3mu^2$$

which is the required
PATH OF A RAY OF LIGHT.

And this,
by integration*
gives, in rectangular coordinates,

$$x = R - \frac{m}{R} \cdot \frac{x^2 + 2y^2}{\sqrt{x^2 + y^2}}$$

for the equation of the curve on
page 280.

Now, since α (page 280) is
a very small angle,
the asymptotes of the curve may be
found by taking y very large by
comparison with x,
and so,
neglecting the x terms on the right
in the above formula,
it becomes

$$x = R - \frac{m}{R} (\pm 2y).$$

And,

*For details see page 90 of
A. S. Eddington's
"The Mathematical Theory of Relativity,"
the 1930 edition.

using the familiar formula for
the angle between two lines
(see any book on Analytics):

$$\tan \alpha = \frac{m_1 - m_2}{1 + m_1 m_2},$$

where α is the desired angle,
and m_1 and m_2 are
the slopes of the two lines,
we get

$$\tan \alpha = \frac{4Rm}{4m^2 - R^2},$$

from which it is easy to find

$$\sin \alpha = \frac{4m}{R + 4m^2}.$$

And, α being small,
its value in radian measure is
equal to $\sin \alpha$,*
so that
we now have

(86) $\qquad \alpha = \dfrac{4m}{R + 4m^2}.$

Now,
what is the actual value of α
in the case under discussion,
in which

$\qquad R =$ the radius of the sun

and

$\qquad m$ is its mass?

*For the proof of this see
any book on calculus,
or look up a table of
trigonometric functions.

Since $R = 697,000$ kilometers,
and $m = 1.47$ kilometers †
$4m^2$ may be neglected by
comparison with R,
so that (86) reduces to the
very simple equation:

$$\alpha = \frac{4m}{R}$$

from which we easily get

$$\alpha = 1.75 \text{ seconds.}$$

In other words,
it was predicted by
the Einstein theory
that,
a ray of light passing near the sun
would be bent into a curve (ACF),
as shown in the figure on p. 280,
and that,
consequently
a star at A would
APPEAR to be at B,
a displacement of
an angle of 1.75 seconds!
If the reader will stop a moment
to consider
how small is an angle of
even one DEGREE,
and then consider that
one-sixtieth of that is
an angle of one MINUTE,
and again
one-sixtieth of that is

†See page 315.

an angle of one SECOND,
he will realize how small is
a displacement of 1.75 seconds!

Furthermore,
according to the Newtonian theory,*
the displacement would be
only half of that!
And it is this TINY difference
that must distinguish
between the two theories.

After all the trouble that
the reader has been put to,
to find out the issue,
perhaps he is disappointed to learn
how small is the difference
between the predictions of
Newton and Einstein.
And perhaps he thinks that
a decision based on
so small a difference
can scarcely be relied upon!
But we wish to point out to him,
that,
far from losing his respect and faith
in scientific method,
he should,
ON THE CONTRARY,
be all the more filled with
ADMIRATION AND WONDER
to think that
experimental work in astronomy
IS SO ACCURATE
that

*See the footnote on p. 278.

these small quantities* are measured
WITH PERFECT CONFIDENCE,
and that they
DO distinguish
between the two theories and
DO decide in favor of the
Einstein theory,
as is shown by the
following figures:
The British expeditions, in 1919,
to Sobral and Principe,
gave for this displacement:

$$1.98'' \pm 0.12''$$

and

$$1.61'' \pm 0.30'',$$

respectively;
values which have since been
confirmed at other eclipses,
as, for example,
the results of Campbell and Trumpler,
who obtained,
using two different cameras,

$$1.72'' \pm 0.11'' \text{ and } 1.82'' \pm 0.15'',$$

in the 1922 expedition of the
Lick Observatory.

So that by now
all physicists agree that
the conclusions are
beyond question.

*See also the discrepancy in
the shift of the perihelion
of Mercury,
on page 275.

We cannot refrain,
in closing this chapter,
from reminding the reader that
in 1919
there was a World War,
and that
Einstein was then classified as
a GERMAN scientist,
and yet,
the British scientists,
without any of the
stupid racial prejudices then
(and alas! still)
rampant in the world,
went to a great deal of trouble
to equip and send out expeditions
to test a theory by
an "enemy."

XXXIV. THE THIRD OF THE "CRUCIAL" PHENOMENA.

We have already seen that
two of the consequences from
the Einstein theory
were completely verified by
experiment:

(1) One, concerning the shift of
the perihelion of Mercury,
the experimental data for which
was known long before Einstein
BUT NEVER BEFORE EXPLAINED.
And it must be remembered
that the Einstein theory was

NOT expressly designed to
explain this shift,
but did it
QUITE INCIDENTALLY!

(2) The other, concerning the bending
of a ray of light as it
passes near the sun.
It was never suspected
before Einstein that
a ray of light when passing
near the sun
would be bent.*
It was for the first time
PREDICTED by this theory,
and, to everyone's surprise,
was actually verified
by experiment,
QUANTITATIVELY as well as
QUALITATIVELY (see Chap. XXXIII).
Now there was still another
consequence of this theory which
could be tested experimentally,
according to Einstein.
In order to appreciate it
we must say something about spectra.

Everyone probably knows that
if you hang a triangular glass prism
in the sunlight,
a band of different colors,
like a rainbow,
will appear on the wall where
the light strikes after it has
come through the prism.
The explanation of this phenomenon

*But, see the footnote on p. 278.

is quite simple,
as may be seen from the diagram:

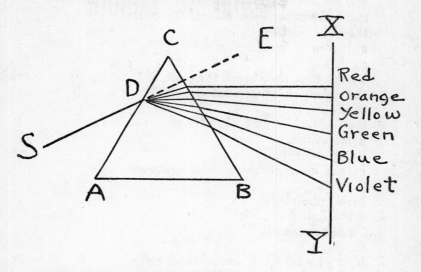

When a beam of white light, *SD*,
strikes the prism *ABC*,
it does NOT continue in
the SAME direction, *DE*,
but is bent.*
Furthermore,
if it is "composite" light,
like sunlight or any other white light,
which is composed of
light of different colors
(or different wave-lengths),

*This bending of a light ray
is called "refraction,"
and has nothing to do with
the bending discussed in Ch. XXXIII.
The reader may look up "refraction"
in any book on elementary physics.

291

each constituent
bends a different amount;
and when these constituents
reach the other side, *BC*, of the prism,
they are bent again,
as shown in the diagram on p. 291,
so that,
by the time they reach the wall, *XY*,
the colors are all separated out,
as shown,
the light of longest wave-length,
namely, red,
being deflected least.
Hence the rainbow-colored spectrum.

Now, obviously,
if the light from *S* is
"monochromatic,"
that is,
light of a SINGLE wave-length only,
instead of "composite,"
like sunlight,
we have instead of a "rainbow,"
a single bright line on *XY*,
having a DEFINITE position,
since the amount of bending,
as we said above,
depends upon the color or wave-length
of the light in question.
Now such monochromatic light
may be obtained from
the incandescent vapor
of a chemical element —
thus sodium, when heated,
burns with a light of
a certain definite wave-length,
characteristic of sodium.

And similarly for other elements.
This is explained as follows:
The atoms of each element
vibrate with a certain
DEFINITE period of vibration,
characteristic of that substance,
and, in vibrating, cause
a disturbance in the medium around it,
this disturbance being
a light-wave of definite wave-length
corresponding to
the period of vibration,
thus giving rise to
a DEFINITE color
which is visible in
a DEFINITE position in the spectrum.
And so,
if you look at a spectrum
you can tell from the bright lines in it
just what substances
are present at S.

Now then,
according to Einstein,
since each atom has
a definite period of vibration,
it is a sort of natural clock
and should serve as
a measure for an "interval" ds.
Thus take ds to be
the interval between
the beginning and end of one vibration,
and dt the time this takes,
or the "period" of vibration;
then, using space coordinates
such that

$$dr = d\theta = d\phi = 0\ ,$$

293

that is,
the coordinates of an observer
for whom the atom is vibrating at
the origin of his space coordinates
(in other words,
an observer traveling with the atom),
equation (71) becomes

$$ds^2 = \gamma dt^2 \text{ or } ds = \sqrt{\gamma}\, dt\,,$$

where $\qquad \gamma = 1 - \dfrac{2m}{r}$ (see p. 253).

Now,
if an atom of, say, sodium
is vibrating near the sun,
we should have to substitute
for m and r
the mass and radius of the sun;
and, similarly,
if an atom of the substance is
vibrating near the earth,
m and r would then have to be
the mass and radius of the earth,
and so on:
Thus γ DEPENDS upon
the location of the atom.
But since ds is
the space-time interval between
the beginning and end of a vibration,
as judged by an observer
traveling with the atom,
ds is consequently
INDEPENDENT of the location
of the atom;
then, since

$$ds = \sqrt{\gamma}dt\,,$$

obviously *dt* would have to be
DEPENDENT UPON THE LOCATION.

Thus,
though sodium from a source
in a laboratory
gives rise to a line in
a definite part of the spectrum,
on the other hand,
sodium on the sun, which,
according to the above reasoning,
would have a
DIFFERENT period of vibration,
and hence would emit light of a
DIFFERENT wave-length,
would then give a bright line in a
DIFFERENT part of the spectrum
from that ordinarily due to sodium.

And now let us see
HOW MUCH of a change in
the period of vibration
is predicted by the Einstein theory
and whether it is borne out
by the facts:
If *dt* and *dt'* represent
the periods of vibration near
the sun and the earth,
respectively,
then

$$ds = \sqrt{\gamma_{\text{sun}}}\, dt = \sqrt{\gamma_{\text{earth}}}\, dt'$$

or

$$\frac{dt}{dt'} = \frac{\sqrt{\gamma_{\text{earth}}}}{\sqrt{\gamma_{\text{sun}}}}.$$

Now γ_{earth} is very nearly 1;
hence

$$\frac{dt}{dt'} = \frac{1}{\sqrt{\gamma_{sun}}} = \frac{1}{\sqrt{1 - \dfrac{2m}{R}}}$$

$$= \frac{1}{1 - \dfrac{m^*}{R}} = 1 + \frac{m^*}{R}.$$

Or, using the values of
m and R given on page 286,
we get

$$\frac{dt}{dt'} = 1 + \frac{1.47}{697,000} = 1.00000212.$$

This result implies that
an atom of a given substance
should have a
slightly LONGER period of vibration
when it is near the sun than
when it is near the earth,
and hence a
slightly LONGER wave-length
and therefore
its lines should be
SHIFTED a little toward the
RED end of the spectrum (see p. 292).

This was a most unexpected result!
and since the amount of shift
was so slight,

*Neglecting higher powers of $\dfrac{m}{R}$

since $\dfrac{m}{R}$ is very small

(see the values of m and R on p. 286).

it made the experimental verification
very difficult.

For several years after
Einstein announced this result (1917)
experimental observations on this point
were doubtful,
and this caused many physicists
to doubt the validity of the
Einstein theory,
in spite of its other triumphs,
which we have already discussed.
BUT FINALLY, in 1927,
the very careful measurements
made by Evershed
definitely settled the issue
IN FAVOR OF THE EINSTEIN THEORY.

Furthermore,
similar experiments were performed
by W. S. Adams
on the star known as
the companion to Sirius,
which has a relatively
LARGE MASS and SMALL RADIUS,
thus making the ratio

$$\frac{dt}{dt'} = 1 + \frac{m}{r}$$

much larger than
in the case of the sun (see p. 296)
and therefore easier to observe
experimentally.
Here too
the verdict was definitely
IN FAVOR OF THE EINSTEIN THEORY!

So that to-day

all physicists are agreed
that the Einstein theory
marks a definite step forward
for:

(1) IT EXPLAINED
PREVIOUSLY KNOWN FACTS
MORE ADEQUATELY THAN
PREVIOUS THEORIES DID (see p. 103).

(2) IT EXPLAINED FACTS
NOT EXPLAINED AT ALL
BY PREVIOUS THEORIES
such as:
(a) The Michelson-Morley experiment,*
(b) the shift in the perihelion
of Mercury (see Ch. XXXI),
(c) the increase in mass of
an electron when in motion.†

(3) IT PREDICTED FACTS
NOT PREVIOUSLY KNOWN AT ALL:
(a) The bending of a light ray
when passing near the sun (see Ch. XXXII).
(b) The shift of lines in
the spectrum (see p. 296).
(c) The identity of mass and energy,
which, in turn,
led to the ATOMIC BOMB!
(See p. 318 ff.)

And all this
by using
VERY FEW
and

*See Part I, "The Special Theory."
†See Chap. VIII.

VERY REASONABLE
hypotheses (see p. 97),
not in the slightest degree
"far-fetched" or "forced."

And what greater service
can any physical theory
render
than this !

We trust that the reader
has been led by this little book
to have a sufficient insight
into the issues involved,
and to appreciate
the great breadth and
fundamental importance of
THE EINSTEIN THEORY OF RELATIVITY!

XXXV. SUMMARY.

I. In the SPECIAL Relativity Theory
it was shown that
two different observers,
may, under certain
SPECIAL conditions,
study the universe from their
different points of view
and yet obtain
the SAME LAWS and the SAME FACTS.

II. In the GENERAL Theory,
this democratic result was found to
hold also for
ANY two observers,
without regard to the
special conditions mentioned in I.

III. To accomplish this
Einstein introduced the
PRINCIPLE OF EQUIVALENCE,
by which
the idea of a FORCE OF GRAVITY
was replaced by
the idea of the
CURVATURE OF A SPACE.

IV. The study of this curvature
required the machinery of
the TENSOR CALCULUS,
by means of which
the CURVATURE TENSOR was derived.

V. This led immediately to
the NEW LAW OF GRAVITATION
which was tested by
the THREE CRUCIAL PHENOMENA
and found to work beautifully!

VI. And READ AGAIN
pages 298 and 299!

THE MORAL

THE MORAL

Since man has been
so successful in science,
can we not learn from
THE SCIENTIFIC WAY OF THINKING,
what the human mind is capable of,
and HOW it achieves SUCCESS:

1. There is NOTHING ABSOLUTE in science.
Absolute space and absolute time
have been shown to be myths.
We must replace these old ideas
by more human,
OBSERVATIONAL concepts.

II. But what we observe is
profoundly influenced by
the state of the observer,
and therefore
various observers get
widely different results —
even in their measurements of
time and length!

III However,
in spite of these differences,
various observers may still
study the universe
WITH EQUAL RIGHT
AND EQUAL SUCCESS,
and CAN AGREE on
what are to be called
the LAWS of the universe.

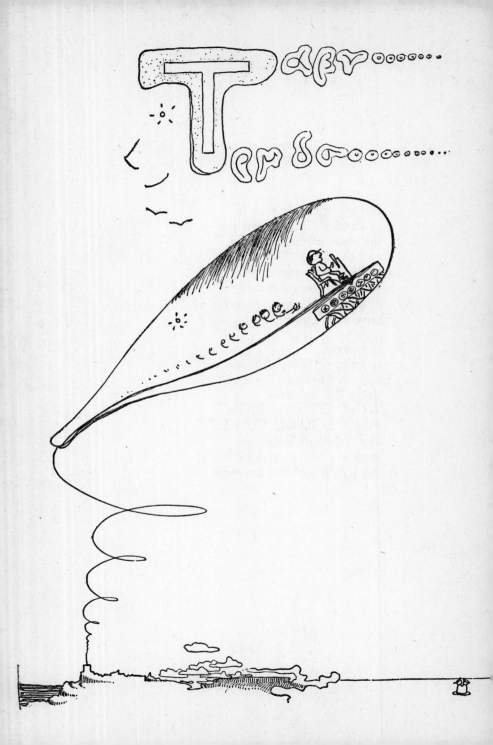

IV. To accomplish this we need
MORE MATHEMATICS
THAN EVER BEFORE,
MODERN, STREAMLINED, POWERFUL
MATHEMATICS.

V. Thus a combination of
PRACTICAL REALISM
(OBSERVATIONALISM)
and
IDEALISM (MATHEMATICS),
TOGETHER
have achieved SUCCESS.

VI. And
knowing that the laws are
MAN-MADE,
we know that
they are subject to change
and we are thus
PREPARED FOR CHANGE.
But these changes in science
are NOT made WANTONLY,
BUT CAREFULLY AND CAUTIOUSLY
by the
BEST MINDS and HONEST HEARTS,
and not by any casual child who
thinks that
the world may be changed as easily
as rolling off a log.

WOULD YOU LIKE TO KNOW?

I. HOW THE EQUATIONS (20) ON PAGE 61 ARE DERIVED:

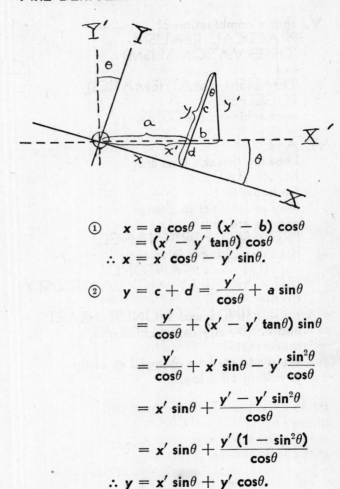

① $\quad x = a\cos\theta = (x' - b)\cos\theta$
$\quad\quad = (x' - y'\tan\theta)\cos\theta$
$\quad \therefore x = x'\cos\theta - y'\sin\theta.$

② $\quad y = c + d = \dfrac{y'}{\cos\theta} + a\sin\theta$

$\quad\quad = \dfrac{y'}{\cos\theta} + (x' - y'\tan\theta)\sin\theta$

$\quad\quad = \dfrac{y'}{\cos\theta} + x'\sin\theta - y'\dfrac{\sin^2\theta}{\cos\theta}$

$\quad\quad = x'\sin\theta + \dfrac{y' - y'\sin^2\theta}{\cos\theta}$

$\quad\quad = x'\sin\theta + \dfrac{y'(1 - \sin^2\theta)}{\cos\theta}$

$\quad \therefore y = x'\sin\theta + y'\cos\theta.$

310

• II. HOW THE FAMOUS MAXWELL EQUATIONS LOOK:

$$\begin{cases} \dfrac{1}{c}\dfrac{\partial X}{\partial t} = \dfrac{\partial N}{\partial y} - \dfrac{\partial M}{\partial z} \\[2ex] \dfrac{1}{c}\dfrac{\partial Y}{\partial t} = \dfrac{\partial L}{\partial z} - \dfrac{\partial N}{\partial x} \\[2ex] \dfrac{1}{c}\dfrac{\partial Z}{\partial t} = \dfrac{\partial M}{\partial x} - \dfrac{\partial L}{\partial y} \end{cases}$$

$$\begin{cases} \dfrac{1}{c}\dfrac{\partial L}{\partial t} = \dfrac{\partial Y}{\partial z} - \dfrac{\partial Z}{\partial y} \\[2ex] \dfrac{1}{c}\dfrac{\partial M}{\partial t} = \dfrac{\partial Z}{\partial x} - \dfrac{\partial X}{\partial z} \\[2ex] \dfrac{1}{c}\dfrac{\partial N}{\partial t} = \dfrac{\partial X}{\partial y} - \dfrac{\partial Y}{\partial x} \end{cases}$$

X, Y, Z represent the components of the ELECTRIC FORCE at a point x, y, z in an electromagnetic field, at a given instant, t.

L, M, N represent the components of the MAGNETIC FORCE at the same point and at the same instant.

311

III. HOW TO JUDGE
WHETHER A SET OF QUANTITIES
IS A TENSOR OR NOT:
We may apply various criteria:

(1) See if it satisfies any of
the definitions of tensors of
various character and rank
given in (16), (17), (18), etc.,
or in (30), (31), etc.
or in (32), etc.

Or

(2) See if it is the
sum, difference, or product
of two tensors.

Or

(3) See if it satisfies
the following theorem:
A QUANTITY WHICH
ON INNER MULTIPLICATION
BY ANY COVARIANT VECTOR
(OR ANY CONTRAVARIANT VECTOR)
ALWAYS GIVES A TENSOR,
IS ITSELF A TENSOR.
This theorem may be
quite easily proved
as follows:
Given that XA_α is known to be
a contravariant vector,
for any choice of
the covariant vector A_α ;
To prove that X is a tensor:
Now since XA_α is
a contravariant vector,
it must obey (16), thus:

$$(X'A'_\beta) = \frac{\partial x'_\delta}{\partial x_\gamma} (XA_\alpha);$$

but $\quad A'_\beta = \dfrac{\partial x_\alpha}{\partial x'_\beta} A_\alpha$

or $\quad A_\alpha = \dfrac{\partial x'_\beta}{\partial x_\alpha} A'_\beta,$

hence, by substitution,

$$X' A'_\beta = \frac{\partial x'_\delta}{\partial x_\gamma} \cdot \frac{\partial x'_\beta}{\partial x_\alpha} A'_\beta X$$

or

$$A'_\beta \left(X' - \frac{\partial x'_\delta}{\partial x_\gamma} \cdot \frac{\partial x'_\beta}{\partial x_\alpha} X \right) = 0.$$

But A'_β does not have to be zero, hence

$$X' = \frac{\partial x'_\delta}{\partial x_\gamma} \cdot \frac{\partial x'_\beta}{\partial x_\alpha} X$$

which satisfies (17),
thus proving that
X must be a
CONTRAVARIANT TENSOR
OF RANK TWO.

And similarly for other cases:
Thus if $X A^\alpha = B_{\beta\gamma}$
then X must be a tensor of
the form $C_{\alpha\beta\gamma}$;
and if $X A_\alpha = C_{\sigma\tau\rho}$,
then X must be a tensor of
the form $B^\alpha_{\sigma\tau\rho}$,
and so on.

Now let show that
the set of little g's in (42)
is a tensor:

Knowing that ds^2 is a
SCALAR —
i.e. A TENSOR OF RANK ZERO —
(see p. 128),
then
the right-hand member of (42) is also
A TENSOR OF RANK ZERO;
but dx_ν is, by (15) on p. 152,
A CONTRAVARIANT VECTOR,
hence,
by the theorem on page 312,
$g_{\mu\nu}\, dx_\mu$ must be
A COVARIANT TENSOR
OF RANK ONE.
And, again,
since dx_μ is
a contravariant vector,
then,
by the same theorem,
$g_{\mu\nu}$ must be
A COVARIANT TENSOR
OF RANK TWO,
and therefore
it is appropriate to write it
with TWO SUBscripts
as we have been doing
in anticipation of
this proof.

IV. WHY MASS CAN BE EXPRESSED IN KILOMETERS:

The reader may be surprised to
see the mass expressed in kilometers!
But it may seem more reasonable
from the following considerations:
In order to decide in what units
a quantity is expressed
we must consider its "dimensionality"
in terms of the fundamental units of
Mass, Length, and Time:
Thus the "dimensionality" of
a velocity is L/T;
the "dimensionality" of
an acceleration is L/T^2;
and so on.
Now, in Newtonian physics,
the force of attraction which
the sun exerts upon the earth
being $F = kmm'/r^2$ (see p. 219),
where m is the mass of the sun,
m' the mass of the earth,
and r the distance between them;
and also, $F = m'j$,
j being the centripetal acceleration
of the earth toward the sun
(another one of the fundamental
laws of Newtonian mechanics);
hence

$$\frac{kmm'}{r^2} = m'j$$

or $\qquad m = \frac{1}{k} r^2 j.$

Therefore,

the "dimensionality" of m is

$$L^2 \cdot \frac{L}{T^2} = \frac{L^3}{T^2}$$

since a constant, like k,
has no "dimensionality."
And now
if we take as a unit of time,
the time it takes light to go
a distance of one kilometer,
and call this unit
a "kilometer" of time
(thus 300,000 kilometers would
equal one second, since
light goes 300,000 kilometers in
one second),
then we may express
the "dimensionality" of m thus:
L^3/L^2 or simply L;
thus we may express
mass also in kilometers.
So far as considerations of
"dimensionality" are concerned,
the same result holds true also for
Einsteinian physics.
If the reader has never before
encountered this idea of
"dimensionality"
(which, by the way, is a very
important tool in scientific thinking),
he will enjoy reading a paper on
"Dimensional Analysis" by
Dr. A. N. Lowan,
published by
the Galois Institute of Mathematics
of Long Island University in
Brooklyn, N. Y.

$$G_{11} = \{11, 1\}\{11, 1\} + \{11, 2\}\{21, 1\} +$$
$$\{11, 3\}\{31, 1\} + \{11, 4\}\{41, 1\} +$$
$$\{12, 1\}\{11, 2\} + \{12, 2\}\{21, 2\} +$$
$$\{12, 3\}\{31, 2\} + \{12, 4\}\{41, 2\} +$$
$$\{13, 1\}\{11, 3\} + \{13, 2\}\{21, 3\} +$$
$$\{13, 3\}\{31, 3\} + \{13, 4\}\{41, 3\} +$$
$$\{14, 1\}\{11, 4\} + \{14, 2\}\{21, 4\} +$$
$$\{14, 3\}\{31, 4\} + \{14, 4\}\{41, 4\}$$

$$-\frac{\partial}{\partial x_1}\{11, 1\} - \frac{\partial}{\partial x_2}\{11, 2\}$$

$$-\frac{\partial}{\partial x_3}\{11, 3\} - \frac{\partial}{\partial x_4}\{11, 4\}$$

$$+\frac{\partial^2}{\partial x_1 \, \partial x_1} \log \sqrt{-g}$$

$$-\{11, 1\} \frac{\partial}{\partial x_1} \log \sqrt{-g}$$

$$-\{11, 2\} \frac{\partial}{\partial x_2} \log \sqrt{-g}$$

$$-\{11, 3\} \frac{\partial}{\partial x_3} \log \sqrt{-g}$$

$$-\{11, 4\} \frac{\partial}{\partial x_4} \log \sqrt{-g}$$
$$= 0.$$

If this mathematics BORES you
BE SURE TO READ
PAGES 318-323!

THE ATOMIC BOMB

We saw on p. 78 that the energy
which a body has when at rest, is:

$$E_0 = mc^2.$$

Thus, the Theory of Relativity
tells us not only that
mass and energy are one and the same
but that, even though they are the same
still, what we consider to be
even a SMALL MASS is
ENORMOUS when translated into ENERGY terms,
so that a mass as tiny as an atom
has a tremendous amount of energy —
the multiplying factor being c^2,
the square of the velocity of light!
How to get at this great storehouse of
energy locked up in atoms
and use it to heat our homes,
to drive our cars and planes,
and so on and so on?
Now, so long as m is constant,
as for elastic collision,
E_0 will also remain unchanged.
But, for inelastic collision,
m, and therefore E_0, will change;
and this is the situation when
AN ATOM IS SPLIT UP, for then
the sum of the masses of the parts
is LESS than the mass of the original atom.
Thus, if one could split atoms,
the resulting loss of mass would
release a tremendous amount of energy!
And so various methods were devised
by scientists like Meitner, Frisch,
Fermi, and others

to "bombard" atoms.
It was finally shown that when
Uranium atoms were bombarded with neutrons* ¹
these atoms split up ("fission")
into two nearly equal parts,
whose combined mass is less than
the mass of the uranium atom itself,
this loss in mass being equivalent,
as the Einstein formula shows,
to a tremendous amount of energy,
thus released by the fission!
When Einstein warned President Roosevelt
that such experiments might lead to
the acquisition of terrific new sources of power
by the ENEMY of the human race,
the President naturally saw the importance
of having these experiments conducted
where there was some hope that
they would be used to END the war
and to PREVENT future wars
instead of by those who set out to
take over the earth for themselves alone!
Thus the ATOMIC BOMB
was born in the U.S.A.

And now that a practical method
of releasing this energy
has been developed,
the MORAL is obvious:
We MUST realize that it has become
too dangerous to fool around with
scientific GADGETS,
WITHOUT UNDERSTANDING
the MORALITY which is in

* Read about these amazing experiments in
  "Why Smash Atoms?" by A. K. Solomon,
  Harvard University Press, 1940.

319

Science, Art, Mathematics —
SAM, for short.
These are NOT mere
idle words.
We must ROOT OUT the
FALSE AND DANGEROUS DOCTRINE
that SAM is amoral
and is indifferent to
Good and Evil.
We must
SERIOUSLY EXAMINE SAM
FROM THIS VIEWPOINT.*

Religion has offered us
a Morality,
but many "wise guys" have
refused to take it
seriously,
and have distorted its
meaning!
And now, we are getting
ANOTHER CHANCE—
SAM is now also
warning us that
we MUST
UNDERSTAND the MORALITY which
HE is now offering us.
And he will not stand for
our failure to accept it,
by regarding him merely as
a source of gadgets!
Even using the atomic energy
for "peaceful" pursuits,

*See our book
"The Education of T. C. Mits"
for a further discussion
of this vital point.

321

$$E_0 = mc^2.$$

like heating the furnaces in
our homes,
IS NOT ENOUGH,
and will NOT satisfy SAM.
For he is desperately trying
to prevent us from
merely picking his pockets
to get at the gadgets in them,
and is begging us to see
the Good, the True, and
the Beautiful
which are in his mind and heart.
And, moreover,
he is giving
new and clear meanings to
these fine old ideas
which even the sceptical
"wise guys"
will find irresistible.
So
DO NOT BE AN
ANTI-SAMITE,
or SAM will get you
with his
atomic bombs,
his cyclotrons,
and all his new
whatnots.
He is so anxious to HELP us
if only we would listen
BEFORE IT IS TOO LATE!

SOME INTERESTING READING:

(1) "The Principle of Relativity" by Albert Einstein and Others. Published by Methuen and Company, London.

(2) The original paper on the Michelson-Morley experiment: Philosophical Magazine, Vol. 24 (1887).

(3) "The Theory of Relativity" by R. D. Carmichael. Pub. by John Wiley & Sons., N. Y.

(4) "The Mathematical Theory of Relativity" by A. S. Eddington, Cambridge University Press (1930).

(5) "Relativity" by Albert Einstein. Published by Peter Smith, N. Y. (1931).

(6) "An Introduction to the Theory of Relativity" by L. Bolton. Pub. by E. P. Dutton & Co., N. Y.

(7) Articles in the Enc. Brit., 14" ed., on: "Aberration of Light" by A. S. Eddington, and "Relativity" by J. Jeans.

(8) "Relativity Thermodynamics and Cosmology" by R. C. Tolman. Pub. by Clarendon Press, Oxford.

(9) "The Absolute Differential Calculus" by T. Levi-Civita. Pub. by Blackie & Son, London.

(10) "Calculus of Variations" by G. A. Bliss. Open Court Pub. Co., Chicago.

(11) "The Meaning of Relativity" by Albert Einstein. Princeton University Press, 1945

(12) "The Law of Gravitation in Relativity" by Levinson and Zeisler. Pub. by Univ. of Chicago Press.